Medieval English Medicine
AD 500–1300

STANLEY RUBIN

Medieval English Medicine

DAVID & CHARLES NEWTON ABBOT LONDON
VANCOUVER
BARNES & NOBLE BOOKS NEW YORK
(a division of Harper & Row Publishers, Inc)

For
Muriel, Marion and Roger

This edition first published in 1974
in Great Britain by
David & Charles (Holdings) Limited
Newton Abbot Devon
in the USA by
Harper & Row Publishers Inc
Barnes & Noble Import Division

0 7153 6704 8 (*Great Britain*)
06 4960161 (*United States*)

Printed in Great Britain by
Latimer Trend & Company Ltd Plymouth

Contents

5

List of Illustrations

The illustrations are reproduced by kind permission of the following:

Bodleian Library, Oxford, for plates on pages 102, 119, 120
British Museum for plates on pages 33, 34, 51, 52, 101

Preface

In this survey of the sources and materials for the medical history of early England, I have had the general reader in mind as much as those with a special interest in the subject. I have, moreover, tried to depart from the more conventional approach to medical history so often limited to the study of specific diseases or their treatment throughout the ages. Instead, I hope I have succeeded, by the extensive use of quotations, in presenting as complete and accurate a picture as primary evidence permits of disease, sickness and medical practice in their widest sense during one particular period. An attempt has also been made, wherever possible, to emphasise how disease and its consequences were seen through contemporary eyes – a social aspect of medical history frequently neglected.

Should any explanation be required for what may seem to be the arbitrary fixing of the beginning of the fourteenth century as the concluding date for this survey, it is simply that I have aimed at showing that, by this time, the evidence is becoming progressively more divorced, both medically and historically, from that provided by the earlier material with which the book is primarily concerned. A medico-historical watershed had been reached and to go further would seriously upset the historical balance and presentation of the sources.

While I have received many kindnesses during the

preparation of this book, I should like to record my appreciation in particular to Dr D. P. Kirby, MA, FR HistS of the Department of History, University College of Wales, Aberystwyth, for his never-failing help and advice extended to me over a long period of time. I am indebted also to Dr Calvin Wells for the benefit of his expert knowledge of ancient disease, to Professor A. R. Myers who so kindly made it possible for me to use the facilities of the Library at the University of Liverpool, and to the staff of the Borough of Crosby's Public Library for their assistance. I need hardly say that any shortcomings are my own responsibility; indeed in a field where evidence is so sparse, errors will doubtless occur and interpretations must remain uncertain.

It is hoped that the select bibliography will be found useful in addition to the very full references and notes which are provided, not only to acquaint the reader with the available evidence, but to encourage him to seek out for himself the primary source material which is, after all, the very essence of history and is ignored at one's peril.

S.R.

Introduction

As the Roman forces were compelled to withdraw from Britain during the fifth century in order to defend their hard-pressed continental empire from the almost overwhelming attacks of the invading Germanic barbarian hordes, the era of the great folk movements was in full flood.

The Romans left behind them in Britain a Romanised British upper stratum of society whose leaders were highly civilised and imbued with the ideals and styles of Roman culture. They were, however, unable adequately to defend their towns and countryside from the renewed depredations of their ancient enemies, the Picts and Scots from the North, who now saw Britain undefended and an easy target for plunder.

In desperation, some of these Romano-British leaders called in continental Saxon mercenaries to help them repulse their enemies and permitted the newcomers to settle in the eastern part of the country. In this they were pursuing a policy previously adopted by the Romans when they had governed Britain, but gradually more Saxons came and settled in what must have appeared, at a time of much pressure of peoples and land shortage in Europe, a rich and attractive country.

Bede, in his *Ecclesiastical History*, refers to an epidemic of virulent plague which spread throughout Britain about the year 440, which was the cause of such mortality, he reports, that there were scarcely enough healthy men left to bury the dead. It is intriguing to speculate whether it was this serious loss of manpower which could have been a principal reason for the British leaders calling in Saxon reinforcements and also the ease with which the latter occupied their new lands.

These mercenaries and their paymasters soon quarrelled and the Anglo-Saxons (as they can now be called) began to settle in the country on a more permanent basis. As the fifth century progressed, other leaders accompanied by their war bands began to spread up the river valleys, extending their settlements over an ever-increasing area of the island.

They came, according to Bede, from areas now known as the Schleswig-Jutland peninsula and Northern Germany. His account of this geographical location has been to a large extent archaeologically verified. Pottery and metal work of very similar craftsmanship has been found both in England and in those regions mentioned by Bede. Among the invaders, though not mentioned by Bede, were Franks and Frisians from Belgium and the Netherlands; and early English cemeteries have also yielded their weapons and pottery.

As the barbarians pushed westwards, they swamped much of the Romano-British culture with superstition and magic until, finally, an amalgam of Classical-Teutonic ideas became established. It is this mixture which we see, not only in political and social life, but also in the evolution of Anglo-Saxon medicine.

Groups of warriors gradually combined together under war leaders who slowly but surely occupied clearly defined areas of the country. These leaders began to establish royal dynasties and the areas under their authority began to emerge as kingdoms, some of which had only a transient existence while others survived and prospered. Ultimately seven kingdoms, the 'heptarchy', came to dominate the island: Northumbria, divided in earlier times into northern Bernicia and southern Deira, Mercia in the midlands, Wessex in the south of the country, East Anglia, Essex,

Sussex and Kent. All their kings traced their ancestry back to the pagan god Woden, so appearing as god-descended and possibly possessing magical powers. Woden appears frequently in the Anglo-Saxon medical text *Lacnunga*, and was regarded as a source of good luck, health and victory.

The pagan era of the Anglo-Saxons (sixth and seventh centuries) is often reflected in their medicine which, in turn, passed on even earlier traditions brought over with the original settlers from their Germanic homelands.

We shall see how various Teutonic concepts were enshrined in the medical treatises: such ideas, for example, as 'elfshot', an explanation of the sudden onset of illness, the rule of 'nines' or the beneficial effects of numbers, and the concept of the 'worm' which was regarded as the source of much disease, are the most obvious. These, and others, all indicate the preservation of pagan magical ideas and beliefs. It is not difficult to see how these magical traditions originated and they persisted long after the conversion of the population to Christianity.

When these simple and primitive people lived near to undisturbed forest or open and bleak moorland, they readily believed them to be inhabited by giants and other supernatural creatures. There was, in addition, a strong belief in the forces of nature, in the winds and in the earth itself. Nothing was more natural than that all the population, not simply peasants, should seek the aid of such magical powers and unseen creatures in the search for a cure for their ills. They fully accepted the existence of elves and other spirits, both good and evil; they could either call on these for aid or else resort to practices designed to frustrate them. In either case definite remedies were being concocted and applied in the very early days of the history of the Germanic people.

The very strong emphasis on plant lore, clearly seen in so many of their remedies, served to provide not only a means to a cure but sometimes a protection against those invisible beings which were regarded as hurtful and malign. The collection of the herbs and their administration to the patient were frequently accompanied by pagan rites, later to be circumscribed and even replaced by Christian observances. The plant lore and folk medicine of the kind practised by the Anglo-Saxons, though written down as late as the ninth and tenth centuries, were in fact, in many cases, the surviving traditions of the heathen past, sometimes older than the original settlement in Britain, and observed in the old Germanic lands in Europe. We can certainly accept that the Anglo-Saxons preserved a great deal of folk medicine from their forebears.

Before and during the period of the heptarchy, widespread lowland settlements were established; the Anglo-Saxons did not usually destroy the towns which had survived from the Roman period but, possessing only limited building techniques, tended to allow them to fall into ruin. They preferred to settle in small communities along river valleys where the land was fertile and easier to cultivate.

During the first three hundred or so years of Anglo-Saxon England, the average village consisted of some 50 to 150 people, with each settlement frequently existing almost in isolation from its neighbours, since each site had been hacked out separately from the woodland and forest that covered much of the country. By 1066, however, the majority of villages were within walking distance of each other.

The domestic accommodation of the early population consisted of little more than small huts having sunken floors and providing little or no head room. These huts or *grubenhauser*, the name given to this sort of semi-sunken dwelling, were often as small as 12ft by 10ft with the floor 2–3ft below ground level, so that cramped conditions were endured by all but the wealthy or noble few. Refuse would quickly accumulate and general squalor prevailed. Disease would spread unchecked in such an environment and only their partial isolation enabled villagers to avoid the worst effects of the numerous epidemics which occurred. Domestic hygiene was impossible under these conditions and infectious diseases and others caused by squalor and dirt would have been common and widespread. The processes of infectious diseases were quite outside the comprehension of the Anglo-Saxon or his physician, so no attempt could possibly be made to eradicate them. All too often outbreaks of such diseases just had to run their course. As time went on, dwelling standards improved but, except for the wealthy classes, domestic accommodation was never anything better than crude, uncomfortable and overcrowded.

In addition to these domestic difficulties, throughout the entire period under review, periodic famine and malnutrition was the fate of the population; hence life for the ordinary citizen was a very hard existence, balanced on the thin edge between survival and disaster.

With the coming of Christianity to England in 597, a new source of medical knowledge appeared. Missionaries from Rome who came with Augustine, or who followed later, would almost certainly have brought some medical knowledge and, as religious ceremonies became established, medical practice slowly incorporated Christian rites and rituals. Several texts demonstrate the early stages of this development whereby pagan and Christian traditions and practices existed side by side and remedies were prescribed which contained elements of both. At first, heathen recommendations appeared which contained a very superficial Christian overlay, gradually followed by those exhibiting a more obvious religious character though still frequently retaining pagan features. The latter can clearly be seen in the various taboos, in belief in disease transference, and in many other mystic concepts.

Religious elements, both pagan and Christian, retained their influence throughout the whole period of Anglo-Saxon medicine and the priest was often involved in helping to effect a cure. The large body of Christian literature, particularly the *Lives* of the various saints, contains many examples of the sick being taken to these holy men for their help and intercession. Faith healing, or at least a strong belief in the healing abilities of pious men, was a major factor in Anglo-

Saxon medicine. The prevailing view that illness was the penalty for sin resulted in a strong religious element in its treatment.

Prayers, paternosters and incantations offered up by the leech himself accompanied many of the suggested remedies, together with a great deal of superstitious matter which is found both in the medical texts and in the general literature of the time. When the leech went out to gather his herbs, he recited Christian prayers but did not always give up his appeals to pagan deities. For example, when he or his patient was instructed to observe silence while gathering the herbs, or forbidden to look behind him, the worship of the forces of nature was not very far removed from his mind.

The history of England from the seventh to the eleventh centuries is a story of gradual accumulation of power by single kingdoms, first by Northumbria, then by Mercia and finally by Wessex. At the close of the eighth century, a new element entered the English scene. The pagan Vikings from Scandinavia began to raid the coastal areas and, as easy plunder became ever more attractive, armies of Norse or Danish raiders began to stay over the winters and ultimately settled in the eastern and northern parts of the country in such numbers that the territory became known as the *Danelaw*. Scandinavian paganism began to feature in the folklore of the region and elements of it soon entered into medical doctrines and concepts. These traditions tended to ignite the embers of residual heathenism which had persisted from pre-Conversion times.

Slowly, however, these settlers accepted Christianity and were brought under the control of the English kings of Wessex, as Alfred the Great (871–99) and his successors gradually extended the boundaries and influence of their West Saxon kingdom. The whole country had become a single partially unified kingdom by the time of King Eadred's death in 955. In the reign of Ethelred the Unready in the late tenth century, the Vikings again began their attacks and so successful were they that by 1016 the Scandinavian Prince

Cnut had ascended the English throne. On his death, his two sons reigned for a short time, after which, in 1042, Edward the son of Ethelred was crowned and the English royal line was thus restored. It was the death of Edward the Confessor without an heir which produced the crisis of Earl Harold's accession and Duke William of Normandy's successful bid for the throne in 1066 at Hastings, a battle waged for the attractive and desirable kingdom he considered his by right.

It was during these last two centuries, the tenth and eleventh, that England witnessed the revival of its monasteries under the energetic leadership of such church dignitaries as Dunstan, Aethelwold and Oswald. Medical facilities were established in the monastic infirmaries and monks as physicians were foremost among medical practitioners. The care of the sick became a specific duty of the monasteries and there is little doubt that many medical manuscripts were produced in the peace and quiet observed within their walls, where advances in patient care could take place in an orderly environment.

In early medieval times, medicine, like other disciplines, remained static for long periods; any developments, when they did occur, extended over many years and took a similarly lengthy time to spread over the country. In this way, for the country as a whole, Anglo-Saxon medicine survived the Norman Conquest and was not subjected to any significant changes by Norman medical practice. The Norman occupation was spread thinly over the country and the ordinary citizen carried on his normal life much as before. It would be the local leech to whom he would go for advice and attention when required, the very practitioner trained and nurtured in the Anglo-Saxon medical tradition. It was not until the thirteenth century that new influences began to emerge or, at any rate, take root, as the Arabic system of medicine became more widely available in England. A new medical atmosphere was then created where some standards of clinical observation and more rational attempts at treating disease

B

became established; these new methods and ideas and their principal English practitioners will be discussed in the last chapter of this book. By their time, however, except for residual vestiges, Anglo-Saxon medical practice had virtually disappeared before the advancing late medieval medical 'enlightenment'.

I

Archaeological Evidence

The peoples who were later to become the Anglo-Saxons came to this country, as we have seen, from north-western Europe; but who were these tribes in the ethnic or racial sense? Did anything distinguish them from earlier or later inhabitants of the British Isles? What was their physical appearance and stature and did their living habits force any skeletal or functional adaptations? From what diseases did they suffer and can their life span or mortality rates be calculated? It is now possible tentatively to suggest answers to these and other related questions fundamental to the understanding of the medical background of Anglo-Saxon and Norman England. It is important to stress at the outset that many conclusions cannot yet be regarded as certain, though evidence is slowly accumulating which allows reasonable grounds for the general acceptance of some, at least, of the answers to the above questions.

Archaeologists excavating Anglo-Saxon settlement sites containing skeletal remains and, in particular, burial grounds and cemeteries, have provided much bony material from which the present state of our knowledge largely stems. It is from this skeletal material that the answers to the questions just posed may be attempted.

ANTHROPOLOGY

When a group of individuals are discovered and excavated and their skulls or crania survive both time and the spade in reasonably good condition, it is possible to establish the basic type of cranium possessed by any particular individual. Crania are grouped into three broad categories according to various measurements and indices calculated from complex and detailed analyses of the bones. One of the principal indices is the *cranial index* which is calculated from the formula: $\dfrac{maximum\ parietal\ width}{maximum\ parietal\ length} \times 100$, the parietal bones being the two which form the sides and roof of the skull. Skulls which produce a result of less than 75 are regarded as being *dolichocranial* or longheaded; those whose cranial index lies between 75 and 79·9 are *mesocranial*; and skulls whose index is 80 or more are considered *brachycranial* or broadheaded.

From these cranial indices, broad racial groupings become possible. If, for example, in an area where all previous populations are known to have been dolichocranial, a group of brachycranial individuals is found, this may indicate an intrusive racial element. Moreover, it may be possible to establish the geographical origin of this group if other similar brachycranial groups are known to have existed in certain other areas. Perhaps these intrusive skulls belonged to a marauding war band operating far from their homeland? Perhaps their owners came into the country from a different region of the European mainland than those already inhabiting the area in question? These and similar questions of origin may be cautiously interpreted once sufficient anthropological details are available. It must be emphasised, however, that what will be discussed here is very much an oversimplification; but it is possible that, used with care, craniometric indices in conjunction with other anthropological data can help as a guide to racial origins and movement of peoples and may even point to general patterns of settlement.

In the British Isles, the cranial index for each of the following main racial groups of inhabitants has been calculated, making it possible to indicate the racial origins of the Anglo-Saxons:

	Mean cranial index	
Neolithic man (*c* 4000–2000 BC)	71·7	dolichocranial
Bronze Age man (*c* 2000–700 BC)	82·0	brachycranial
Iron Age man (*c* 700 BC–AD 100)	75·8	dolichocranial
Anglo-Saxons (*c* AD 500–AD 1100)	74·9	dolichocranial
17th-cent English (White chapel, London)	75·1	dolichocranial
20th-cent English	approx 77·5–78·2	mesocranial

These indices show little alteration from the Iron Age to modern times; the only brachycranial group was Bronze Age man. Many other cranial measurements show a difference between the Bronze Age and the other groups. This significant difference in cranial index suggests that the Bronze Age people were of a distinctly different racial stock from both their predecessors and those who followed them. This Bronze Age type disappeared by the time of the Iron Age invasion, though some evidence of brachycephaly exists in modern Scottish crania, indicating a greater infusion of the brachycranial type in Scotland than in England.

With regard to specific Anglo-Saxon crania, the vast majority of those recorded show that only one racial group is represented: a dolichocranial type showing evidence of a rugged muscular development. There is no significant difference between skulls belonging to Saxons, Angles or Jutes and, as far as the Anglo-Saxon population of the sixth century and earlier is concerned, all the evidence points to all three belonging to a single homogeneous racial group. Moreover, even if the Viking or Scandinavian invaders are included, little cranial difference is apparent.[1] For later Anglo-Saxon material, again no distinction is found between it and the earlier inhabitants, so confirming the homogeneous nature of the various tribes and groups who settled in the country. Even after the eleventh century, the Normans made little difference as their numbers were never very great, and, in any case, of those who were actually from Normandy and not mercenaries from other areas, many were of a similar type, being of Viking origin.

Groups of individuals have been found, however, whose cranial indices do not conform to those expected for their time or place and this can cause obvious difficulty in establishing positively the group's origin. For example, at Red Castle, Thetford, the community found there, though of apparent Anglo-Saxon origin, were predominantly brachycranial. This broadheadedness was to become more widespread in the later Middle Ages and because, as we have seen, the Anglo-Saxons were basically dolichocranial, there remains the uncertainty as to the identity of the Red Castle people. Their cranial indices are more appropriate to a later, post-Conquest date and, indeed, bear a similarity to other, fourteenth to fifteenth century groups from Hythe in Kent and Rothwell in Northamptonshire.[2]

The whole question of cranial and other interpretations is still in doubt and most racial hypotheses suggested by previous generations of anthropologists are not fully acceptable to most modern authorities. Until further research produces evidence based on more solid grounds, no definite conclusions are possible and the whole subject of racial origin must remain imprecise.[3]

Another means of attempting to identify the Anglo-Saxons is from a study of their mandibles and palates which enables certain deductions to be made about the physical appearance of these people. For instance, if the width of the palate is measured from material ranging in date from prehistoric to modern times, the more recent English palatal width has decreased when compared with that of previous periods. The mean Neolithic male palatal width measurement is 40·2mm, while that for the Anglo-Saxons is 41·3mm and for the seventeenth-century Whitechapel people 39·6mm. A possible cause of this decrease in palatal width in more modern times was the introduction of softer foods, resulting, for some people, in a reduced palatal function; hence the possibility of reduced growth and the narrowing of the jaws. However, here again a definitive explanation has not yet been advanced and the reason for these changes remains obscure.

During the time that the palatal width has been decreasing, and certainly since the Anglo-Saxon period, there has been an accompanying increase in the vaulting or height of the palate which has produced a notable effect upon the appearance of the modern English face. This increased vaulting has resulted in a tendency to narrowing and elongation of the face, a narrowing of the nose as well as the decreased width of the palate.[4] This development could possibly account for the modern tendency to crowding of the teeth and other dental irregularities.

Perhaps more significant are the findings associated with Anglo-Saxon mandibles or jaw bones. The upper front teeth, the incisors, are found to meet the lower incisors in an edge-to-edge bite and do not show the modern overlapping bite where the lower front teeth are well overlapped and partially covered by the upper incisors. This edge-to-edge bite produces a characteristic attrition of the back teeth as they appear to have been used in a grinding fashion. Thus, the edges of the incisor teeth would tend to slide upon one another in a side-to-side manner and the molars would be compelled to move likewise, hence the characteristic damage found on these teeth.

There seems little doubt that the development from the edge-to-edge bite to the present overlapping position is mainly due to modern methods of cooking. Once the eating of raw or partially cooked foods became unnecessary, the tendency to the overlapping bite began to appear. As food became softer and more easily digestible, the need for the more powerful molar grinding action was reduced in much the same way as palatal width diminished.

The stature or height of populations can now be determined with some accuracy; the Anglo-Saxon population are thought to have been, in general, just a little shorter than modern English men and women, although even this small difference in stature has recently been questioned.[5]

Stature statistics, of course, vary from place to place and the few examples cited here have been chosen at random, but some idea of the physical appearance of the Anglo-Saxons should emerge.

At Little Eriswell, Suffolk, the population excavated show an average height for males of 5ft 8in, and for females 5ft 2¼in.[6]

The group from Red Castle, Thetford, already referred to show a mean male height of 5ft 6¾in, and for females, 5ft 2¼in, while the relevant figures from a cemetery near Horndean, Hampshire, show the average male height as 5ft 7½in, females 5ft 4in.[7]

It has been estimated that the average stature generally for the Anglo-Saxons is about 5ft 6½in for men and 5ft 0½in for women[8] (average modern English male 5ft 7in; female 5ft 2½in), corroborated almost exactly by the statistics at Bidford-on-Avon, Warwickshire[9] and at Polhill, Kent, where the average male stature is 5ft 6in and the female 5ft 2in.[10]

SKELETAL ADAPTATION

Bones of Anglo-Saxon individuals frequently display changes in their shape which suggest some skeletal adaptation in response to a particular function. One of the more common changes is that of *platymeria* of the femur, shown by an excessive compression or flattening of the bone from front to back: an actual yielding of the bone at some point along the upper part of its shaft. Platymeria seems no longer to be a feature in modern femura and it is therefore regarded as being the result of very strong muscular activity producing the extra compression force, now no longer common as vigorous activity is less necessary. As the degree of platy-meria has steadily decreased from prehistoric to modern times, this would tend to verify quantitatively how the need for vigorous overactivity of the musculature has decreased as living standards have been raised and life has become less dependent upon vigorous muscle power.

Another anatomical variation in some Anglo-Saxon skeletons is *platycnemia* of the tibia. This feature is shown by an increase in the antero-posterior dimensions of the bone and is the result of postural habits. Professor Cameron con-siders that platycnemia develops during adolescence and is caused by retroversion, or the forcing backwards of the upper end of the tibia due to prolonged periods in the squatting position, though this is another hypothesis not universally accepted. This tibial retroversion, it is suggested, alters the direction of the downwards thrust from the femur, hence the tibia is compelled to increase its antero-posterior dimensions in order both to resist and compensate for this abnormal femoral pressure. In this way varying degrees of platycnemia are produced.[11] On the other hand, it has been suggested that both platymeria and platycnemia are due to a deficiency in bone minerals in the areas of muscle attach-ments. It is likely that the diet of early people could be responsible for these variations.[12]

The fibulae show evidence to suggest that the muscles of the legs were robust and developed. In a group of Anglo-Saxons from Guildown, Surrey, for example, a roughened area was often found on the posterior aspect of the upper third of the fibula at the origin of the soleus muscle, indicat-ing an active and powerful muscle.

The bones of the foot similarly exhibit general evidence of the great strength and strong use of the leg muscles. The areas of muscle attachment on each bone are frequently more developed than is now the case and are the result of the pull due to strong muscular activity, as well as from the increased rapidity of limb movement required in former times. The inherent instincts of speed, alertness and rapidity of movement, not only in defence, but in hunting and other essential activities, could well have been vital for survival.

An interesting development which illustrates one feature of early Anglo-Saxon social life is the common appearance of the 'squatting facet' on the lower end of the tibia. This facet develops after prolonged adoption of the squatting position and is found less frequently in later Saxon times, suggesting that better living standards were being enjoyed and the use of chairs and benches was becoming more common. At Little Eriswell, Suffolk, for instance, no less than seven out of ten individuals show evidence of squatting facets at the ankle joint. This high proportion must indicate poor economic and domestic standards. At North Elmham, Norfolk, of a group of 206 persons dating from 950 to 1050, as many as 66 (80·0 per cent) of the women and 34 (40·5 per cent) of the men display squatting facets,[13] indicating not only that the group were living in relative poverty but that the women endured a ruder, less comfortable existence than the men, and that whatever comforts may have been available, the men had first claim. Possibly this high proportion of female facets was due to the habit of squatting for long periods weaving cloth and performing other crafts and duties.

An additional feature resulting from habitual squatting is the extension present on the articular surface of the medial condyle of the femur on its posterior surface. Long periods of squatting with the resulting extreme degree of knee flexion would be enough to produce this articular elongation.

MORBIDITY AND MORTALITY

The amount of skeletal material now available makes possible a brief review of the morbidity or general state of health of the Anglo-Saxons. Moreover, reasonably reliable statistics are available for life spans and mortality rates.

As the age at death is closely related to living standards, prevalence of disease and poverty, these conditions can often be deduced from mortality data. The age at death of an individual can be determined fairly accurately from a study of any surviving teeth, particularly in the case of children from the state of dental eruption and in adults from the degree of tooth wear or attrition. Estimates of age can also be calculated from the degree of union achieved in certain joints such as those of the pelvis and the sacral vertebrae, from evidence shown by the cranial sutures and from the extent of the epiphyseal union or calcification of long bones. For example, in the sacrum the union of vertebral bodies begins at about 16 years of age and proceeds from the lowest vertebra upwards and union is usually completed by about 23 years of age. In the case of a skull, certain cranial sutures, particularly the basi-sphenoid suture, begin to close when the individual approaches the age of about 17 to 18 years and the gap is closed by about the age of 21 to 23 years.

As far as long bones are concerned, epiphyseal union of the arm bones occurs at about 18 years; that of the leg bones at about 19 years of age. Similarly, the pelvic bones and clavicle can be used to estimate skeletal age. In the pelvis, the union of the ischium and pubic bones takes place at about 7 to 9 years, while the three bones which make up the acetabulum or socket of the hip joint, the ilium, ischium and pubis, are united by the age of 14 to 16 years.

For older age groups other criteria apply. For example, from the ages of 30 to 50 years, the sacrosciatic ligament begins to ossify and after about 40 years of age, vertebral lipping may also be present. While the foregoing is only a slight indication of what is possible, experts are able to estimate skeletal age at death with considerable accuracy.

It should be emphasised at this point that all morbidity and mortality patterns resulting from the examination of skeletal remains must be used with care. While communication between communities, especially in later Anglo-Saxon England, may have been closer than has hitherto been supposed, the data produced from one region or from one population cannot be assumed to be relevant to other areas or communities. Generalised and wide-ranging conclusions are to be avoided and evidence relating to any particular material should not be attributed automatically to other skeletal remains.

Factors unknown to us may well have influenced any specific community. Could the skeletons, for example, be those of a warrior band killed in battle, when the average age would tend to be lower than that of the general population? Were the individuals perhaps the victims of an epidemic or a disease especially virulent in the younger age group? Moreover, what have been the effects of the haphazard survival and discovery of the bones upon the overall mortality statistics? Unfortunately no really satisfactory answers are yet possible.

There is, however, one general observation which may be made. For the country as a whole, the average age at death of Anglo-Saxon communities is very low compared with that of modern England (71 years).

Among the Red Castle, Thetford, people, the average age at death was 33·9 years (males 38·1; females 30·4), and of their children, 87·5 per cent had died by the age of 6 years.[14] It is worth noting here that of the children found at North Elmham, Norfolk, whose peak age at death was between 2 and 4 years, nearly 49 per cent had died by the age of 6 years, which is only just over half the figure for Thetford; while the Thetford peak age of childhood death was as low as from birth to 2 years. Thus, of the Thetford children, only about 12·5 per cent survived after the age of 6 years, compared with 51 per cent of the North Elmham children – a very significant difference in mortality. On the other hand, it should be pointed out that a definite increase occurs in the number of North Elmham children who died after the age of twelve whereas there is a gradual and steady decrease in the number of children of similar age who died at Thetford, viz,

Age	% Thetford	% North Elmham
0–6	87·5	49·0
6–12	12·5	23·1
12–18	0·0	25·9

It is clear, therefore, that the children of Thetford found great difficulty in surviving their early years of life, but having done so could face the future with some confidence. Those from North Elmham, however, seem to have possessed some inborn resistance at first, or perhaps had received a nourishing diet, only to fall victims to disease and death later in childhood and adolescence.

The considerably lower female age of death typical of all Anglo-Saxon communities, and indeed of most ancient societies, has frequently been attributed to the risks and complications of childbirth. There could, of course, be additional reasons for this early female demise. Girls and women may not have received the same standards of nutrition as men, especially in the warrior-orientated society that existed in early England. Males would probably have had first call upon whatever supplies of wholesome food were available. Females could also have been at special risk from the hard physical labour that would have been expected of them. Furthermore, it is likely that males, from the time they were born, were brought up with more care and consideration than was extended to their sisters; this would also be in keeping with primitive behaviour patterns.

The peak age at death of a population from Polhill, Kent (*c* AD 600), was between 25 and 30 years, with the average age being 24 years, considerably lower than that of the Red Castle population; while the peak age at death at Breedon-on-the-Hill, Leicestershire (*c* AD 800), was 35 to 40 years, with an average of 31 years.[15]

At North Elmham (*c* AD 950–1050), the average age at death was 38 years for males and 36 for females, a combined mean age of 37 years, a somewhat higher figure than that for other East Anglian populations. For example, the mean age at death at Red Castle, Thetford, was 33·9 years; the late Saxons of St Catherine, Thorpe, Norwich, averaged 34·1 years; and for the middle era group of Anglo-Saxons from Caister-on-Sea, the average age was 34·7 years.

A community at Winnall, Hampshire, show their greatest

mortality between the ages of 15 and 30 years which is a very low figure. Moreover, no less than 20 per cent of this population had died by early adolescence; thus only about one half lived on after their twenties. In spite of the generally earlier female age of death, it is remarkable that of those who lived to old age at Winnall, three out of four were women.[16]

The people from Little Eriswell, Suffolk, similarly died young. Of 34 individuals, only 4 had survived to 35 years of age; 14 had died between the ages of 20 and 35, and 8 before adolescence.

From the evidence now available and as the above random sample tends to verify, the population living in Anglo-Saxon England suffered a 50 per cent mortality rate by the age of about 30 years, while some 90 per cent had died by the age of 50 years.

Some confirmation of these mortality figures may be seen from the ages at death of well-known persons of the period. King Alfred, for instance, died when he was 50 years of age; Ethelred II was about 48, Athelstan was between 40 and 50, Edgar only 31 and Cnut about 40 when they died. These rather low ages at death, even amongst those enjoying the highest living standards of their times, suggest that the average peasant was not likely to survive to any great age.

Nevertheless, there were exceptions. Archbishop Theodore, who came to England in the seventh century when he was about 67 years old, lived for a further 21 years; King Ethelbert of Kent was no less than 70 when he died; St Wilfrid lived until he was 75 years old; Bede's friend and teacher, Ceolfrith, Abbot of Jarrow, was 74 when he died; and other examples exist to show that, although the general population certainly suffered from a high mortality rate, including some from the very highest social class, there were still some who lived to a ripe old age.

It is useful to compare the above-quoted Anglo-Saxon ages at death with those for people living some four or five centuries later. Instead of the average male age at death lying between 20 and 35 years, it has been estimated that in

England during the thirteenth to fourteenth centuries, the life expectancy at birth was 35 years (the upper end of the Anglo-Saxon scale), while if the infant survived its first year, it could expect to live for an average of 40 years and, even if it lived to this age, could reasonably anticipate a further 18 years of life.[17] Clearly, improved standards of nutrition, housing and general vitality were beginning to assert their beneficial effects.

A remarkable aspect of mortality and morbidity patterns is the considerable difference sometimes found between communities existing not only at the same time but also in close geographical proximity. The morbidity pattern, or the rate and prevalence of disease, at Caister-on-Sea, Norfolk, for instance, is significantly higher than that for Burgh Castle for each year of a child's life up to about the age of ten, at which age the rate for Burgh Castle increases and overtakes that for Caister. Thus, although Burgh Castle and Caister are only some five miles apart, the Caister children suffered proportionately more illness before they reached the age of ten years, while those from Burgh Castle experienced their maximum morbidity after that age even though they still suffered from less illness in absolute terms. This early vitality of the Burgh Castle children could perhaps be due to the fact that there are indications that some, at least, of their parents were dairy farmers, able to provide their children with a good nutritional start in life. Certainly no cases of rickets have been found among them.

These morbidity statistics are made possible by the phenomenon known as *Harris's lines*. These lines are clearly seen on radiographs of the tibia (and radius) and appear as transverse lines across the lower end of the bone. They occur as lines of calcification laid down whenever a temporary arrest in growth takes place during an illness, infection or famine and while their number indicates the frequency of pathological disturbances or diseases, they do not suggest the nature or identity of the illness. However, due to the fact that the position of any of the Harris's lines in relation to the end of the bone indicates the length of the diaphysis (shaft of the bone) at the time it was laid down, it is possible to estimate the age of the child at that particular time. Cautiously used and always bearing in mind the many, as yet, indefinite factors as well as the evidence now emerging which suggests that much more attention needs to be given to this subject, Harris's lines may not only provide a record of the more serious illnesses from which a child suffered, but may also suggest the age at which these ailments occurred.[18]

From such data, a start may be made in providing comparisons for the prevalence, persistence and distribution of childhood illness between one region and another and, from them, further evidence concerning the social life of the population may be determined. Further questions arise, however: do the number of Harris's lines bear any relationship to later adult mortality? Did those populations or groups showing the most lines also experience death at the earliest ages? In short, did illness during the childhood years have any influence on life spans or did the people possess some inherent vitality which overcame their earlier misfortunes and, if so, can these vitality factors be identified? It will require much more research and the discovery of more material, properly examined, before these and similar questions may be answered. Dr Calvin Wells has already pointed out in one example that, although the Caister community has considerably fewer individuals showing no lines at all in their tibiae, and hence a markedly higher general morbidity rate than some other East Anglian populations, their average age at death was nevertheless much the same. It would seem as if, in spite of early childhood difficulties, the Caister group were able to overcome them by the time adulthood was reached.[19]

While it is true that the precise nature of the cause of Harris's lines is impossible to ascertain, periods of malnutrition or famine would clearly be reflected in metabolic disturbances causing growth arrest with consequent laying down of calcified lines in the tibiae. Dysentery was common

Page 33   *Aesculapius, Centaurus and 'Plato' (11th century)*

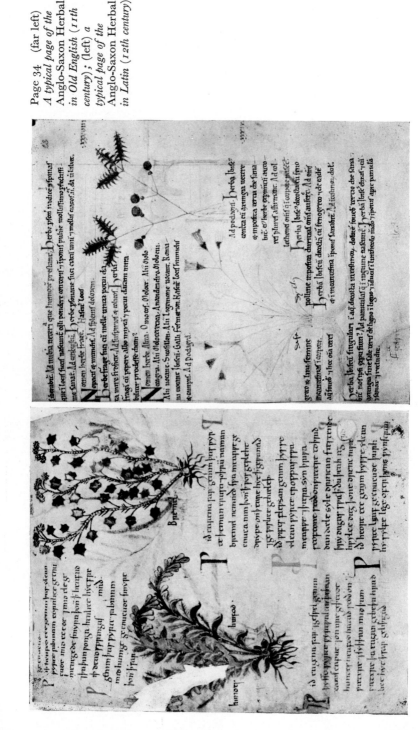

and would also be responsible for many lines as well as the various 'pestilences' which periodically appeared, and while their identification is not possible it is quite likely that some, at least, could have been measles and other childhood ailments which must have been rife but, once overcome, would leave little permanent adverse effects upon general health. Perhaps these illnesses would explain the observation made above that even in populations showing a high rate of Harris's lines, the mean age at death differs little from those with a better history of childhood morbidity. Conditions such as tuberculosis, smallpox and typhus are not thought likely to have been responsible, as they were rarely very active on a widespread scale before *c* 1000, but no definite conclusions about the identity of many of the diseases present in Anglo-Saxon England can yet be drawn.

PALAEOPATHOLOGY

One of the main difficulties in the study of prehistoric and early historic disease is due to the fact that only in those conditions which produce physical change in bones or teeth may a diagnosis be possible. The rest of the bodily tissues soon decay and all pathological evidence is thereby lost. With modern laboratory techniques gradually extending the boundaries of diagnosis, an increase in our knowledge of ancient disease and more definite conclusions may be expected. In particular, pathological changes in bone tissue itself can now be examined and blood disorders, blood groupings and hormonal changes are all now giving up their secrets, though much remains to be done.

A second difficulty is that it cannot be taken for granted that diseases familiar today existed in earlier times, or that particular illnesses produced the same symptoms then as now. That changes may have taken place is suggested by the fact that weather conditions in England during the years *c* 600–1250 were approximately 1–2° C warmer than today; olive trees were grown here in the eighth and ninth centuries

c

and only after about the year 1000 did the weather begin to get cooler. Hence, disease types and their transmission could have been different from those known today, especially as some are liable to be influenced and altered by a warmer climate. It is almost certain that malarial fever existed in marshy areas of early England, for example in the Fens and on the south coast, and no doubt other diseases of warmer climates may have flourished. Indeed, in Norfolk even today there are various species of mosquito which could well act as potential carriers of malaria should the temperature increase by a couple of degrees or so. 'Ague', commonly mentioned in medieval literature, was probably a type or variant of this disease, in addition to referring to various kinds of fever.

While TB and typhus do not appear to have been much of a problem before *c* 1000, there can be little doubt that TB at least became prevalent after this time, due, in no small part, to the increasing population being cramped into un-hygienic conditions, made worse by varying degrees of malnutrition. In these later times, and probably earlier too, diseases of the ears and chronic sinusitis were present, for skulls exist which clearly demonstrate evidence of maxillary, frontal and nasal sinus infection. Therefore, cases of infected sinuses producing descending infection into the chest must have been quite common in the Anglo-Saxons, leading to chronic bronchitis and pneumonia.

Probably the most common disease suffered by the Anglo-Saxons was osteoarthritis. That osteoarthritic changes were common is not surprising as this degenerative joint condition is often associated with occupational stresses and strains, as well as being a process of slow attrition or wearing of the joint surfaces. Farming and rural populations very often suffer from osteoarthritis and, under the conditions prevail-ing in early medieval times, the much increased and strenuous activity imposed upon the joints by farming rough, unbroken ground would surely have taken its toll. The frequent, if minor, irritations and injuries to the joints inevitable under these conditions would also have contributed to the onset and progress of the arthritis. Even walking over rutted, untreated paths and tracks would put all the leg and foot joints at great risk and, as has been pointed out earlier in the chapter, the joints of the foot and ankle do, in fact, show evidence of use under considerable strain. Moreover, much widely scattered osteoarthritis is found in the joints of the foot and, in particular, the head of the first metatarsal (big toe) often displays considerable evidence of the disease.

Osteoarthritic changes in the joints of the arm would result from heavy digging, hacking, woodcutting and similar vigorous arm activity while clearing and cultivating the land. It is worthy of note here that although arthritis was so widespread and severe in many cases, its onset must have begun at a relatively early age. While it is now generally regarded as a disease of 'ageing', and as the Anglo-Saxon average age at death was low, it follows that osteoarthritis became active at a much earlier age than is now the case. This, in turn, must point to hard physical activity being the normal lot of the young and adolescent sections of the population.

The widespread incidence of osteoarthritis is confirmed by the statistics available from the anatomical sites most frequently involved. As far as the Anglo-Saxon population are concerned, the joints of the vertebral column appear to be those most likely to be affected and it is common to find ankylosis or joint fusion due to the considerable degree of osteophytosis (excess bony outgrowths) in the dorsal and lumbar regions of the spine. This frequency of spinal osteoarthritis was almost certainly caused by prolonged periods of bending over the spade, the planting of crops by hand, primitive ploughing and the general poor, stooping posture which could be the result of the habitual squatting adopted by many, especially in the earlier years of our period.

The hip and knee joints, surprisingly, are less frequently involved than might be expected, although some femora provide excellent examples of gross arthritic changes, including eburnation of the femoral condyles and osteophyte

formation around their lower ends, while others show typical
lipping and osteophytosis, especially around the femoral
heads. Many tibiae similarly show extensive changes around
their upper articular surfaces and areas of roughening and
lipping are often seen.

The elbow joint is the most common site for osteoarthritis
of the arm, the shoulder being less frequently involved. The
heads of the ribs also show considerable evidence of arthritic
activity. Osteoarthritis of the ankle joint itself is quite rare,
most of the strain upon the feet apparently having been
taken by the joints of the foot and toes, ie the tarsal and
tarsal-metatarsal joints. This is supported by the abundant
evidence of small bony exostoses (outgrowths) resulting
from torn ligaments around these joints, no doubt caused by
prolonged stress and injury.

It is therefore clear that the vigorous physical activity
typical of a primitive agricultural community showed itself
not only in the prevalence of arthritis but also in the sites
affected by it. One can only imagine the pain, stiffness and
disability endured by the individual but, recognising the
crippling tendencies and great pain often associated with the
disease today, one cannot assume that results were any less
unfortunate during the sixth to twelfth centuries. If the leechbooks are any guide, none of the treatments prescribed by
the leeches for arthritis or joint pain can have been of much
use. For instance, Bald's first leechbook recommends that for
'racking pain in the joints' a mixture be prepared of lithwart
and honey and applied to the joint; alternatively, that
wormwood be mixed with tar and fen cress and, after
wringing out the moisture, the residue be bound on to the
sore joint.[20]

Other joint conditions have been diagnosed, in addition to
osteoarthritis. Osteochondritis dissecans (inflammation of
the joint cartilages) was a fairly common complaint, not only
in the knee (femoral condyles) but elsewhere, while occa-
sional cases have been found of congenital dislocation of the
hip, Osgood-Schlatter's disease (inflammation of the tibial

tubercle)[21] and arthritis of the tempero-mandibular joints. This last complaint is almost certainly due to chewing hard, tough meats and foods contaminated with hard particles of grit and stone. There is plenty of evidence, of course, of general injury, fractures of bones being predominant. Fractures were most common in the forearm where the shafts of the radius and ulna were damaged, presumably in attempts at warding off blows to the head. The skull must also have suffered frequent injury, though it is probable that many cases were not of a very serious nature, with healing taking its normal course. Broken ribs, one of the most common fractures, would similarly have healed with little outside assistance.

Fractures of the ankle, also frequently found, and caused by a twisting fall so easily experienced on rough, hard ground, are precisely the sort of accident that produces also the fracture at the wrist and lower end of the forearm now known as the Colles' fracture.

Inflammatory changes in bone tissue are often displayed in ancient bones, suggesting the existence of serious diseases such as osteomyelitis and periostitis. The organisms responsible for these infections are carried in the blood stream and periodically produce acute inflammatory episodes. Chronic bone infection must have had a marked debilitating effect and would very probably have prevented the individual from working for long periods, with disastrous results for his welfare.

Some diseases would tend to become endemic, in particular those resulting from malnutrition when large areas of land were infertile. Transportation of food on any scale was unknown and while some districts were fortunate in having an adequate supply of varied produce and thus suffered little or no effects from malnutrition, other less well endowed areas would experience persistent nutritional disorders.

Mental deficiency has also been recognised from Anglo-Saxon skeletal remains. A suspected case of a mongol has been identified from Breedon-on-the-Hill, Leicestershire, for example, as has a twelfth-century case of microcephaly found in Hythe, Kent. A further example, though not definitely implying mental deficiency, is that of hydrocephalus – the enlargement of the skull due to excess fluid surrounding the brain. This skull was found in a Romano-British burial at Norton, Yorkshire.[22]

Many other examples of various disorders, spinal variations, malformations and deformities, together with some now quite rare conditions, have been diagnosed, but it is most unfortunate that reports describing this material and its examination (if published at all) are distributed over a wide area of literature: medical, historical and archaeological. Great difficulty is therefore experienced in assembling the evidence which does exist into a systematically arranged body of information. If such an arrangement could be achieved, future developments and discoveries could then be noted and added as they arise and a much more rational approach thus made to the study of palaeopathology.

Before leaving the bony evidence for disease during the Anglo-Saxon and Norman periods, it should be noted that tumours are not only a modern problem. The type most commonly found, however, is the benign or harmless osteoma which is merely a small mass of bone; but several cases of malignant disease have been identified.[23] In addition, tuberculosis of the spinal vertebrae has been recognised in several Anglo-Saxon skeletons.

Examination of the teeth and jaws may also provide evidence about ancient disease. Teeth are of a special value in the study of disease in antiquity as they tend to withstand long periods of burial and survive in sufficient numbers to provide reasonably accurate information.

The first notable feature regarding Anglo-Saxon teeth is the very low incidence of dental caries or decay. The frequency of caries in Britain had risen during the Roman occupation, but then fell sharply to a minimum rate during the seventh to tenth centuries. This rate is approximately only one-sixth of that for the present-day adult English population. It is noteworthy that although the overall incidence of Anglo-Saxon dental caries is low, within this figure wide regional variations occur. On the other hand, tooth wear or attrition was widespread and severe in degree and was the result of eating coarse, unrefined and abrasive foods. In fact, many teeth are found grossly worn down to the extent that secondary dentine has been produced and much of the enamel destroyed.

The low incidence of tooth decay is thought to be associated with the absence of both cane and beet sugars in the diet, honey being the only available sweetening agent. Modern teeth are attacked most frequently in their fissures and also at their contact areas by the action of oral bacteria converting sugar into polysaccharides which are regarded as one of the main causes of dental decay. Anglo-Saxon teeth show their largest proportion of cavities just below the gum line or cervical margin. The diet then eaten consisted of much coarse carbohydrate and starch and would be of low solubility, hence substances would not easily enter and remain in the tooth fissures or around the contact areas. The reason for the cervical margins being the areas of maximum decay in Anglo-Saxon teeth is probably due to the lack of oral hygiene with food lodging or being trapped at the necks of the teeth just below the gum, so permitting the production of acids which would encourage and hasten the process of decay.

The rate of caries in Anglo-Saxon teeth increases with age in both deciduous (milk) and permanent teeth, the molars being the most readily affected group.[24]

In spite of the overall low incidence of tooth decay, a considerable amount of oral disease was present in early medieval England. Perhaps the most frequently encountered condition is that of periodontal disease and abscess formation which was the principal cause of tooth loss, a common finding in Anglo-Saxon jaws after the age of about thirty years. Periodontal disease produces a recession of the alveolar bone of the jaws – an absorption of the bone in which the teeth are set. As large amounts of calculus or tartar are very often present, there is little doubt that this is a contributory factor in the causation of periodontal disease. Moreover, as the bone is slowly absorbed, any slight injury due to hard food, sharp bones or grit could easily set up inflammatory changes from which abscess formation and pyorrhoea would result, with consequent tissue breakdown, the appearance of tracts of infection and generalised septic conditions of the mouth and jaw.

It will now be appreciated that from this brief and some-what cursory survey of the archaeological sources for disease in Anglo-Saxon and Norman England much has been omitted and there are many deficiencies. Some topics have merely been mentioned when ideally they should have been treated in depth; the identity of disease has been left vague or not attempted at all and there is the inability to do much more than simply review the types of disease most commonly found in surviving bones.

These deficiencies, it is hoped, will be made good in the not too distant future when all suitable material is not only collected, but more important, properly examined by skilled palaeopathologists, and their reports are made easily available. Only when these examinations are routinely performed may a more complete picture of ancient disease and its effects emerge and the wide gaps in our knowledge be overcome.

2

Medical Sources

Anglo-Saxon literature, whether prose, poetry or devotional,
was of a singularly high standard for its time, not only for its
content and form but also because much of it was written
in the vernacular, ie Old English. In this respect the literature of Anglo-Saxon England, especially during the tenth
and eleventh centuries, was unique. Other European
countries, if they produced a literature at all, did so in
Latin and hence it was read by only a very limited audience,
but English literature in native Anglo-Saxon was available
to a relatively much wider reading population. These works
written in England in the centuries immediately preceding
the Norman Conquest provide a firm indication of the high
standard of culture attained by the people in their own
tongue, before its gradual modification during the years just
before and following the Conquest, when it slowly evolved
into Early and Middle English as seen, for example, in the
works of Geoffrey Chaucer and William Langland.

The specifically medical literature which existed in
Anglo-Saxon times was similarly written in Old English and
is quite remarkable. While much of it has survived the
ravages of time, it is equally certain that much must have
been destroyed and lost in the many disturbances of monastic
libraries, churches and other repositories of manuscript
literature during the succeeding centuries.

43

The main body of medical texts which does survive dates from no earlier than the tenth to twelfth centuries, though it certainly includes copies of earlier works and clearly contains older influences and traditions.

The credit for the flowering of Old English literature is usually given to Alfred the Great, who believed his subjects to be ignorant of Latin as a consequence of the long years of Viking disturbance, when even the majority of the clergy were unable to cope with the simplest religious rites. Thus he encouraged the translation of established Latin works into the vernacular and commissioned many new works to be written directly in Anglo-Saxon. It is interesting to note that the existence of this Anglo-Saxon medical literature indicates that certain groups, at least, were sufficiently literate in their native tongue to understand the frequently detailed instructions, while they need not necessarily have been fluent in Latin. Indeed, it is quite remarkable that these treatises were written at all when it is remembered that during this same period and even for long afterwards, as far as the rest of Europe was concerned, no other vernacular medical literature was produced. Moreover, at this time very little of an original scientific nature, even in Latin, was forthcoming from the continent, and it is therefore no exaggeration to stress and maintain the uniqueness of this Anglo-Saxon achievement.

There are several principal medical manuscripts in existence, together with various shorter texts, including a few loose pages and fly-leaves containing several prescriptions and medical charms. Most of these were collected and published in three volumes edited by Oswald Cockayne in 1864–6.[1] In this monumental work a modern English translation of much of this material is presented, and while in some instances the translation may not meet the demands of more recent standards of scholarship, this does not in any way detract from the success the editor undoubtedly achieved.

Before considering these treatises in detail, it may be pointed out that the multitude of prescriptions, recipes and treatments recommended and their general overall content must be considered in a dispassionate way. They not only indicate the state of medical knowledge of the period, but they provide a rare glimpse into the life and beliefs of the people. It is true that most of this material describes very primitive attempts at producing a body of therapeutic practice, but credit should be given for the attempt having been made at all. The texts should be viewed within the context of their time and place and they cannot profitably be considered in isolation from their environment: they can only reflect the times in which they were written. It is remarkable that such a large body of medical practice was so well recorded for its practitioners. While much of what is to be discussed in this and other chapters may seem crude, distasteful in parts and perhaps even useless from a modern medical point of view, it was, at least, the serious and not ignoble attempt of an early population to alleviate suffering and distress – a not unworthy endeavour. No medical doctrines can be expected outside the intellectual range of knowledge for the period, nor should the value of treatments be considered without reference to the materials which were available at the time. The raw materials of the Anglo-Saxon physician were very largely herbal and it is fruitless to expect his medical practice to reflect anything other than an almost exclusive preoccupation with botanical remedies.

The principal medical manuscripts are as follows:

1 *The Herbarium of Apuleius Platonicus* (MSS Cotton Vitellius CIII; Bodley Hatton 76, Oxford), known as the *Anglo-Saxon Herbal*. There is a continuation of this work taken from Dioscorides.[2]

2 *The Medicina de Quadrupedibus* of Sextus Placitus,[3] remedies based upon animals and their secretions.

3 *The Leechbook of Bald* (MS Royal 12D XVII),[4] a wide variety of leechdoms and remedies.

4 *The Lacnunga* or *Recipes* (MS Harley 585),[5] a varied collection of prescriptions and recipes.

5 *Peri-Didaxeon* or *Schools of Medicine*[6] (MS Harley 6258),

an Anglo-Saxon translation of earlier Classical medical treatises, particularly of the ninth-century Petrocellus text. 6 A collection of miscellaneous remedies, including recipes found on fly-leaves and old bindings, together with various charms having medical significance.[7] In addition, there is a text written c 1110 containing various medical materials (MS 17 St John's College, Oxford).

THE ANGLO-SAXON HERBAL

This work is the largest of the surviving medical manuscripts. It was written in Old English about AD 1000 and is a Christianised version of the original Latin *Herbarium* of Apuleius Platonicus written in about the fifth century. The fact that four manuscripts of the text are extant among the very few remains of Anglo-Saxon literature in general is indicative of its popularity.

The *Herbal* is made up of two parts: the first and longest section, attributed to Apuleius, consists of 132 chapters or paragraphs; it is followed by a section of 51 chapters taken mainly from the work of Dioscorides, who wrote a compilation of botanical drugs, originally in Greek but translated into Latin in the sixth century. This compilation is known as *On Materia Medica*.[8]

Each chapter is concerned with the virtues and properties of a particular herb and in most cases is accompanied on the original manuscripts by a beautifully coloured illustration purporting to represent the plant. They are not at all accurate representations and are, without doubt, copies of copies of earlier manuscripts now lost; whatever likenesses may have originally existed must largely have been lost in their transmission. Some of the illustrations also show, in addition to the plant concerned, various animals, snakes and winged creatures.

Indeed, it becomes apparent that during the ninth and tenth centuries the illustrations of many of the plants had degenerated into mere drawing exercises, for in a medical manuscript of *c* 1120, from Bury St Edmunds, much more accurate drawings appear including some of plants of a foreign origin. Presumably these were now growing in the herb gardens of the monasteries, a development in monastic medical care which will be discussed at some length in a later chapter.

Soon afterwards, however, in the later part of the twelfth century, this higher standard of illustration deteriorated again and plants became purely diagrammatic in form. All trace of naturalistic representation was lost until, by the thirteenth century, there remains hardly any resemblance to the actual appearance of the plants; instead one finds beautifully coloured designs and leafy patterns without any attempt to depict accurately the subject matter.

The first page of the manuscript contains a magnificent illustration in full colour showing, on the right-hand side, a centaur. Tradition has it that this mythological beast was skilled in the practice of medicine, having derived this knowledge from the god Apollo. The centaur is shown receiving a book from 'Plato', obviously meant to represent Apollo; due to religious scruples, the scribe preferred to use the name of Plato instead of Apollo who was perhaps identified too closely with heathenism. The centaur carries some healing herbs, while on the left of the illustration is represented the figure of Aesculapius, the supposed ancestor of Hippocrates, the great physician. Above the human figures are shown various animals such as the boar, wolf, lion and goat. These animals are frequently referred to in Anglo-Saxon medicine, as will be seen when the *Medicina de Quadrupedibus* is discussed. Finally, worm-like figures are in evidence at the bottom of the picture, representing the Saxon concept of the 'worm' which was a creature thought to be a cause of disease.

In the Anglo-Saxon version of the text, the name of the herb usually appears in the vernacular, but occasionally the Latin version or a corrupt copy of the Latin is given; in some cases the Greek form of the plant name may even be included.

Very often, as each plant is named, some indication is given of where it may be found and it is of interest to notice that, in some instances, the Anglo-Saxon translator has actually added material of his own to the original Latin text. For example, in the case of the plant called yarrow, no fewer than eleven paragraphs have been inserted into the Anglo-Saxon version of the text.[9] These additions must suggest a native knowledge of the use of herbs over and above what could be learned from the Latin work which served as the basis for Anglo-Saxon practice. Moreover, there is a further example of plant knowledge on the part of the Saxon writer. In the chapter concerning the properties of the plant wolf's teazle or thistle, the writer states: 'This wort has leaves reversed and thorny . . .'[10] The word 'reversed' is not found in the version written by Dioscorides and was therefore added by one of the translators, who knew this, or had himself observed that the thistle protects its leaves with thorns pointing both backwards and forwards.

On the other hand, there is no doubt that many of the actual names given to the plants by the Saxon scribes and translators were inaccurate. Some of them, being of foreign origin, would be quite unknown to the Anglo-Saxons; the margin of error due not only to the lack of a real acquaintance with many of the plants but also to copying mistakes must have been considerable.[11]

In spite of the many errors which can be found in the names and descriptions given to the plants, there is obviously a real interest in herbs and their curative properties, as well as a genuine awareness and recognition of where these plants may be found, and the details of the conditions best suited for their growth.

It should be remembered, however, that mistranslation from one language into another was without doubt responsible for frequent errors of plant identification and care must be taken to ensure that at least the more obvious sources of error are always kept in mind.

To illustrate the 'atmosphere' of the text, a typical example from the *Anglo-Saxon Herbal* is given here.

CRESS (Nasturtium)
1. In case a man's hair fall out, take juice of the wort which one names nasturtium and by another name cress, put it on the nose, the hair shall grow.
2. This wort is not sown but it is produced of itself in springs and in brooks; also it is written that in some lands it will grow against walls.
3. For a sore head, that is for scurf and for itch, take the seed of this same wort and goose grease, pound together, it draws from off the head the whiteness of the scurf.
4. For soreness of the body [indigestion], take this same wort nasturtium and pennyroyal, soak them in water and give to drink; the soreness and the evil departs.
5. Against swellings, take this same wort and pound it with oil, lay it over the swellings, then take leaves of the same wort and lay them on also.
6. Against warts [boils], take this wort and yeast; pound together, lay on; they will soon be taken away.[12]

From this example it can be seen how the wort or herb cress is recommended for various and dissimilar disorders. The account also indicates where the herb may be found and its method of growth. Other chapters give quite detailed instructions as to where and how the plants can be gathered. In the case of the plant comfrey, for instance, 'it is produced on moors and on fields and also on meadows',[13] and groundsel similarly 'is produced on roofs and about walls'.[14] There are many comments of this kind, giving the reader of the text adequate advice as to where to find his herbs.

The example of cress given above contains six sub-sections or paragraphs, but some herbs are so popular that many paragraphs are written about their healing properties. In the case of the plant known as ashthroat or vervain, there are 12 paragraphs; yarrow occupies 16 sections, while in the case of betony there are no less than 29 paragraphs, with waybroad not far behind with 22 sub-sections.

Very often the section or paragraph concludes on a

curiously optimistic note. Whether this was to inspire confidence in the patient, or whether the patient himself frequently reported exaggerated benefits to avoid further unpleasant (to say the least!) treatment, cannot be known. Perhaps it was nothing more than wishful thinking on the part of the leech.

Examples of this optimism in the *Anglo-Saxon Herbal* may be cited. In the case of vervain: 'for wounds and ulcers . . . take roots of this wort and wrap around the neck, then it will benefit highly'.[15] For the plant called wolf's comb: 'for liver sickness take juice of this wort . . . give to drink in wine . . . wonderfully it benefits'.[16] In the instance of wild lettuce: 'for dimness of the eyes, take the juice of this wort mixed with old wine and with honey . . . from this you will observe a wonderful cure'.[17]

The *Anglo-Saxon Herbal*, notwithstanding its many defects, does present us with a fair picture of the standard of herbal knowledge and practice prevailing in the tenth to eleventh centuries, and must have been a text much in demand by the Anglo-Saxon physician.

THE MEDICINA DE QUADRUPEDIBUS

This Anglo-Saxon translation from a Latin text is closely associated with the surviving Anglo-Saxon texts of the *Herbal* and may be considered a supplement to it. It shows perhaps more closely than any other of the medical treatises the primitive and distasteful side of English Dark Age medicine, not to mention its more futile and absurd aspects.

The *Medicina* is attributed to Sextus Placitus, who lived some time between the fourth and sixth centuries, and is based upon remedies from Galen and other Greek and Roman writers. The text is of only slight value and is concerned with the medical properties thought to be available from animals and their secretions or extracts; many of the prescriptions given would be quite impossible to prepare,

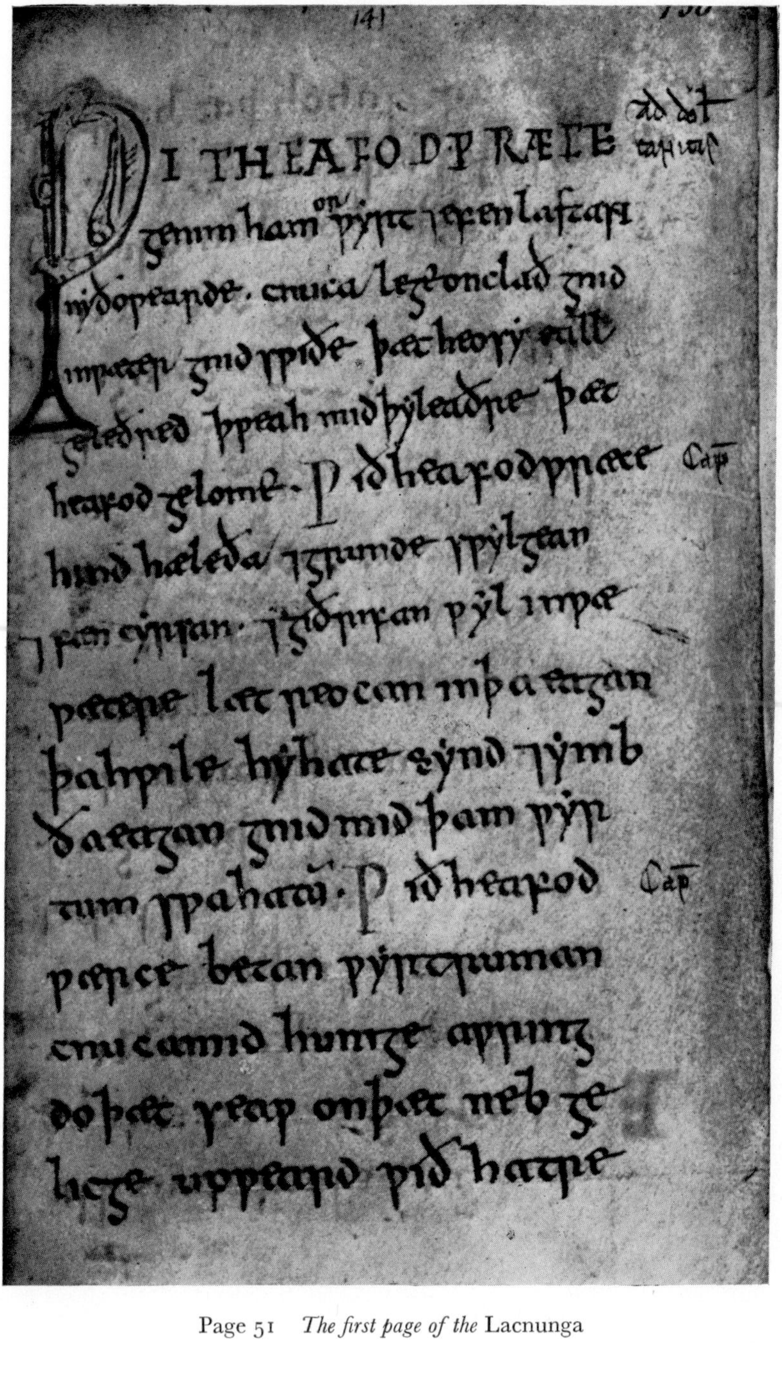

WIÐ HEAFODWÆRCE

(manuscript page of the Lacnunga, Old English text)

Page 51 *The first page of the* Lacnunga

Page 52　(above) *Two warriors being offered medicine by physicians (12th century)*; (below) *surgery for haemorrhoids, nasal polyp and cataract (12th–13th century)*

even in the unlikely event of their containing any useful medicaments.

There are thirteen chapters, some of which contain many paragraphs, and each chapter begins with a drawing of the animal whose virtues are under consideration. For example, in Chapter XI, after a drawing of the bull, there are fourteen paragraphs on how its various secretions or its excrement can assist in healing such diverse conditions as earache (para 5), the removal of ugly marks from the face (para 2), or even the healing of a fractured bone (para 11). The remedies given for these maladies include instructions to make up various mixtures; in the case of earache, it is recommended that drops of bull's gall with honey be inserted into the affected ears. The honey here could well have had some soothing effect. For the removal of facial marks, all that is necessary, apparently, is to smear them with bull's blood; and as far as the fracture was concerned, no more is required to heal it than to 'lay warm bull's dung' on to the fracture site. However, a somewhat more rational treatment for a fracture is to be found in the chapter dealing with the dog. It is suggested that the fracture be bound up with a dog's brain spread upon wool, and left for fourteen days, when it can be expected that it will be greatly improved. It is realised, however, that further improvement will be required and a longer period of 'binding up' or immobilisation will be necessary, and this is accordingly recommended.[18]

A painting of a goat heads Chapter VI, followed by twenty-five paragraphs of recipes using parts of this animal for such disorders as dropsy, cancer, leprosy, headache and insomnia. Also included is a prescription whose object is to assist in the expulsion of the placenta after childbirth! For the reader of the *Medicina*, no more advice is needed for the cure of leprosy than to mix goat's urine with honey and salt and rub the mixture on to the patient's head and body. Should the complaint be insomnia, then 'a goat's horn laid under the head will turn waking into sleep', while the treatment for headache is to procure a new goat's cheese and bind

D

it on the head; this latter treatment apparently never fails, for the paragraph ends with the supremely optimistic words 'it healeth'.

Most of the potions and mixtures given in this text are to be made by mixing the animal extract in oil, honey, water or wine, so creating drinks, or ointments or salves for external application.

The various animals which were considered to be medicinally beneficial and whose use is approved in the *Medicina* are the badger, hart, fox, hare, goat, ram, boar, wolf, lion, bull, elephant and dog. How the lion or elephant is to be obtained is not explained; but of the two paragraphs devoted to the elephant, both concern the supposed virtues of crushed ivory, a commodity that is known to have been imported into this country. Works of art made from ivory were being carved in the late tenth century and in Aelfric's *Colloquy* (tenth century), for example, a merchant mentions ivory as one of the main items he brought back to England.

The *Medicina de Quadrupedibus* indicates clearly one of the beliefs of the Anglo-Saxons regarding disease. It was thought that many diseases and disorders were the work of a demon or evil spirit which had taken possession of the individual. In order to expel this demon, it was necessary to administer medicines so unpleasant that the evil spirit would wish to leave its host's body. Such beliefs led to the production of leechbooks like the *Medicina*, which expressed in prescription form such nauseating medicines and applications as have been briefly outlined. To experience some of these remedies may well have been worse than the disease and it is hard not to feel some sympathy both with the patient who received the treatment and with the physician who would be expected to prepare such unpleasant remedies.

A final point before leaving the *Medicina*: its recommended treatments are not confined to human beings. Cattle and horses are similarly catered for, with recipes derived from the bodies of other animals. For the murrain or pestilence of horses, for example, the treatment advised is to mix badger's blood with salt, and give to the horses by means of a drinking horn for three nights,[19] or alternatively, if the horses are suffering from a fever, then badger's 'suet' is recommended.[20]

THE LEECHBOOK OF BALD

This treatise is the most important piece of medical literature to have survived from the Saxon period. It covers 109 pages or leaves in its manuscript form and 150 pages in the published edition.[21]

The document is in two parts or leechbooks, the first containing 88 chapters and the second 67 chapters. They were written *c* 900–950 from an earlier ninth-century Latin text and following them is a third book consisting of 73 sections which, while written by the same hand, is a separate and additional work. It is probably of similar age to the first two leechbooks, although it is also likely to be a copy of earlier material.[22]

A verse at the end of the second leechbook suggests that this book, together with the first, belonged to a physician or leech known as Bald and was written down by a scribe called Cild.[23] It is not at all certain whether Cild himself was also a physician and was putting down in writing the remedies he had collected and used in his own practice, or whether he was merely a professional scribe writing the book on Bald's instructions, in which case one would assume that the prescriptions were the result of Bald's medical experience.

Each leechbook begins with a long table of contents or chapters which indicate briefly the conditions or illnesses to be discussed and the treatment recommended. This arrangement is in contrast to the *Anglo-Saxon Herbal*, where each chapter concerns itself with a particular herb, and only then the conditions thought to be amenable to its properties.

In the case of the first leechbook, the arrangement is such that Chapter 1 explains the leechdoms for maladies and diseases of the head, and then the book proceeds chapter by chapter down the body until the feet are reached. In this way, the leechdoms for the head, eyes, ears, neck, mouth, teeth, chest, stomach, legs and feet are dealt with and described. There are, in addition, a large group of miscellaneous remedies which complete the book.

The second leechbook, much of which has been taken from Greek and Latin originals, is mainly concerned with internal and abdominal conditions; indeed the first chapter-heading of this book tells us that 'these leechdoms belong to all internal disorders' and there is some slight evidence that attempts have been made at diagnosis and the recognition of signs and symptoms of some diseases.

The stomach, liver, intestines, spleen and various other organs are dealt with, accompanied by recipes and prescriptions thought to heal or alleviate their disorders. Like its predecessor, this leechbook also ends with a collection of varied leechdoms for diseases ranging from gynaecological conditions, jaundice and elephantiasis to headache and stroke. The third leechbook is purely a collection of prescriptions, instructions and advice for a wide variety of diseases, and is sufficiently similar in content and style to the first two books as to give the appearance of a natural supplement to them.

These three leechbooks were obviously intended to be manuals of instruction for the treatment of a bewildering variety of illnesses, injuries, mental states, aches and pains. They contain innumerable instructions for the preparation of herbal mixtures, and interspersed among all these reputed remedies are sections dealing with superstitious rites, charms and invocations which not only reflect the primitive folklore of the people, but, more significantly, show the extent to which residual pagan practices had survived the centuries of Christianity. All these latter prescriptions are aimed at defeating the activities of elves, demons and the like, by the use of both pagan and Christian charms and similar mythological forces, including those which are sometimes found to have a thin overlay of Christian doctrine. Both Greek and Latin heathen traditions are present, as one would expect

considering the origin of considerable portions of the leechbooks, in addition to those practices persisting from the
Germanic and Celtic folklore which the Saxon tribes had
found on their arrival, or brought with them from their
homelands.

It is noteworthy that, while the leechbooks, along with the
Anglo-Saxon Herbal and other medical texts, abound in herbal
prescriptions of all kinds, there are fewer references to herbal
remedies to be found in the earlier literary sources than
might be expected.[24] This could well be the result of the loss
of literary material from the earlier period and the relatively
larger volume of later survival. Notwithstanding this, however, it is quite possible that this paucity could indicate that
the art of English herbalism was developing from a rudi-
mentary and superstitious beginning to what was to become
a common and more sophisticated practice in the tenth and
eleventh centuries.

That the leechbooks were compiled as instructional texts
is also suggested by the various surgical techniques described, and while it is true that these procedures were based
more upon empirical and traditional ideas than on any
knowledge of pathological processes, there is nevertheless
some detailed and rational observation in a few of the
surgical sub-sections. These will be considered later in the
chapter on surgery.

There can be no doubt that, although these books were
intended to be consulted by the physician in his day-to-day
practice, he could not have prepared many of the prescriptions recommended in the leechbooks. Many of these recipes
would have been meaningless to him, while other instructions and advice would have been quite beyond his competence. There are many cases where alternative remedies
are given for the same condition, and hence the leech is
given the appearance of considerable choice, yet large
numbers of the ingredients were of foreign origin and so
would have been almost unobtainable.[25] Moreover, the
number of individual ingredients required to make up a

particular mixture was, in many cases, so great that it would have been impossible to dispense the medicine. There are also several examples in the Anglo-Saxon texts of the use of native or English names for herbs, alongside the classical Roman or Greek names for the same plant. This suggests that some parts, at least, of these treatises were more in the nature of writing exercises, without any thought being given to their real meaning and pharmaceutical use.

A remarkable feature of the leechdoms is the almost complete lack of recognition that treatment may vary with the progress of the patient. No consideration is given to any change in treatment, nor to the quantity of the medicine to be administered as the disease progresses favourably or otherwise.

It is very difficult, if not impossible, to group into types or systems the many disorders and maladies mentioned in the leechbooks. Some names given to diseases are beyond identification, though of course many can be named with reasonable certainty. For example, 'gall disease' or 'yellow disease' must indicate jaundice;[26] 'circle adle [disease]' is shingles;[27] and 'a fiend sick man'[28] is one thought to have been possessed by the devil – another example of pagan magical influence persisting into the tenth century.

Other more obviously descriptive names for diseases can be mentioned: 'half dead disease'[29] is an accurate description of hemiplegia or stroke; 'heart wark [pain]' and 'breast wark'[30] indicate some form of chest and heart pain, possibly such as angina, while 'neck ratten' is thought to refer to scrofula or tubercular glands[31] and 'poc adle' is the name given to smallpox.[32]

The leechbooks, as have already been indicated, provide ample evidence to show that both Greek and Latin influences were operating in the Anglo-Saxon medical world.

It has recently been argued beyond any real doubt that the principal origins of the *Leechbook of Bald* lie in the compilations attributed to Gariopontus, who wrote before the mid-eleventh century, and to Petrocellus, also of the eleventh century. As both these works themselves derive from an earlier, now lost, ninth-century Latin text (whose own origin goes back to Classical writers), it follows that extensive sections of the leechbooks originally stemmed from this ninth-century text.

The real significance of this discussion is that it effectively demolishes the previously established claim that the medical theories of the Salerno school were superior to (and later than) those of Anglo-Saxon medicine. It can now be seen that both schools used the same texts which were circulating in the ninth century and so were clearly in use in England some two hundred years before the date usually considered appropriate for their introduction here.[33]

Some original Classical influences may be seen, for example, in the chapter on pleurisy where certain phrases have been taken directly from the sixth-century Alexander of Tralles.[34] Further, in this illness certain shellfish, such as periwinkles, are recommended; the compiler of the Anglo-Saxon manuscript has copied these from Marcellus Empiricus, who lived at Bordeaux in the fifth century.[35] He was not a physician, and his 'medical' work reaches the lowest point to which medical thought descended during an already bleak period. An illustration of this very inferior quality of Marcellus's advice can be seen from his prescription, again for pleurisy, that the faeces of a boar should be taken in water.[36]

In spite of examples of such debased remedies, there is no doubt that the translator of the *Leechbook of Bald* had a real and wide acquaintance with his material, for it can be shown that he rearranged sections of the work in order to produce a more accurate account of his treatments and was prepared to accept or reject material in line with his understanding of the texts before him. He refused to limit himself to any one source for his recommendations.

Examples of a few of the shorter leechdoms will indicate the type of prescription given and the method adopted to present both symptoms and treatment.

For dropsy, rub betony, as much as a penny-weight in warm water, let the patient drink a good bowl-full daily for three days. Again, take the juice of the roots of ashthroat [vervain] or of dwarf elder, four spoons full, put them into a bowl full of wine and give them to the patient to drink.[37]

Here are wound salves for all wounds and drinks and cleansings of every sort, whether internally or externally. Waybroad beaten and mixed with old lard, the fresh is of no use. Again, a wound salve: take waybroad seed, crush it small, shed it on the wound and soon it will be better.[38]

For a burn, if a man be burned with fire only, take woodruff and lily and brooklime; boil in butter and smear therewith. If a man be burned with a liquid, let him take elm rind and roots of the lily, boil them in milk, smear thereon three times a day. For sunburn, boil in butter tender ivy twigs and smear thereon.[39]

These examples indicate clearly that the general approach of the leechbooks reflects the very low standard to which medicine had descended in the period between the eighth and tenth centuries. Either the more genuine medicine of the world of Hippocrates and Galen had been forgotten, or it had never been translated into Latin. In any case, Greek medicine itself had deteriorated since the time of Galen. It had been replaced by pagan charms, religious rites, and a variety of practices and traditions from folklore such as have been indicated in the work of Marcellus Empiricus.

There is contained in the second leechbook a most interesting passage concerning King Alfred. It would seem that he had requested from the Patriarch Elias of Jerusalem some remedies which this prelate had found to be effective. Unfortunately the beginning of the passage is missing, but there is no doubt as to the sender of the prescriptions and advice nor as to the identity of the recipient. The passage ends with the sentence: 'All this Dominus Helius [Elias], patriarch of Jerusalem ordered to be said to King Alfred.'[40]

It is known that Alfred had communications with the East, for his biographer, Asser, says that 'we have seen and read letters, accompanied with presents, which were sent to him [Alfred] by Abel, the patriarch of Jerusalem'.[41] The name Abel is generally thought to be an error made by Asser in referring to Elias.

Some of the prescriptions sent describe ingredients available only in the Middle East, petroleum for instance, recommended to be drunk for 'inward tenderness' or to be 'smeared on outwardly on a winter's day, since it has much heat'. Balsam, which is also mentioned, is thought to have been unknown in England at this time, but Elias prescribes it as good for the cough and for the treatment of carbuncles.

If, in fact, the reference to presents in Asser's passage included such items as these, then Alfred was certainly acquiring most valuable medicaments, otherwise unobtainable in his kingdom. It is quite likely that Alfred had requested some advice from the patriarch because of his own ill health which had troubled him for many years. As Asser further tells us, from the time Alfred was twenty years of age until he was well over forty, the king had been troubled with an undiagnosed complaint.[42] Presumably, as no relief had been obtained from his English physicians or their medicines, he had been encouraged to look farther afield for advice.

Finally, there is an obvious loss of a section in the second leechbook. In the list of contents at the beginning of this book, under section lx, various gynaecological disorders are referred to, but these are missing from the actual text. This lost section, however, stems from a Hippocratic treatise. Sections lxi, lxii and lxiii are also absent, though the list of contents describes them as dealing with jaundice, elephantiasis, headache and 'dry disease and lung disease'.

This evidence is sufficient to suggest that the Anglo-Saxon leech had access to several remedies for gynaecological conditions, although these almost certainly derive originally from Hippocrates.

THE LACNUNGA

This manuscript contains no illustrations although some letters are illuminated. It is an inferior medical work of 122 chapters of miscellaneous leechdoms which provide many examples of pagan magic, charms and spells, despite its eleventh-century date. The original text must therefore have been earlier, as the *Lacnunga* is rich in these heathen rites and folklore practices. On the other hand, there is no doubt that it also contains sections which show Christian influences and traditions, but these are of a superficial kind and do not really suggest any significant, long-standing or deeply held religious beliefs. It should be appreciated that when the word 'magic' is applied to Teutonic and Anglo-Saxon medicine, it is not used in any derogatory sense. Such practices may well have held some significance, or be derived from rational thinking now lost on the modern reader.

The Northern god *Aesir*, for example, is represented as a protection against 'elfshot' in a poem or lay of totally pagan character.[43] Two further important examples are the *Lay of the Nine Herbs* and the *Lay of the Nine Twigs of Woden*, both of which are about the god Woden and are, therefore, typically heathen poems.[44] All three of these poems have features which confirm their native Teutonic origins. The concept of 'elfshot' was that disease was transmitted by 'elves' which would attack the individual with their 'darts', so producing a disease, the type of which depended upon the nature of the particular elf.

A second indication of the pagan origin of these poems lies in the mystical concern with the number nine. In the *Lay of the Nine Herbs*, each of these herbs has a magical verse sung about it and finally, in its concluding lines, the number nine is frequently repeated:

> These nine darts against nine venoms.
> A snake came crawling, nought did he wound;

> Then took Woden nine twigs of glory . . .
> Now these nine herbs avail against nine spirits
>   of evil.
> Against nine venoms and against nine onfliers
>   [flying venoms or carriers of disease].

It will be noticed, incidentally, that a third Teutonic medical characteristic is displayed in this poem: the concept of 'the worm' which frequently appears in Anglo-Saxon medical texts. The 'worm' was a serpent or snake which, though never precisely described, was thought to cause illness and disease.

Thus in these three poems from the *Lacnunga* there is clear evidence of four of the important early pagan Teutonic medical concepts. There is the concept of the 'elves', the magic associated with the figure nine, that of the 'worm' and fourthly that of the 'flying venoms'. These four beliefs about disease causation appear time and again throughout the *Lacnunga*. There is, for instance, a spell prescribed to combat 'flying venom';[45] a recipe against 'elfshot';[46] and a curious mixture of pagan and Christian traditions in a charm to help an elfshot horse.[47]

The sections which contain purely Christian characteristics mention such things as saints' names which are recommended to be sung, spoken or written, prayers to be recited and various Christian rites to be performed.[48]

A remarkable example of a mixed pagan and Christian charm is contained in a paragraph concerned with preparing a 'holy salve'. After instructions are given to write the names of the saints Matthew, Mark, Luke and John with a spoon in a herbal mixture, it is necessary to perform 'the worm chant' and sing this nine times and then 'put your spittle on them . . .'.[49] The mention here of spittle or saliva reveals yet another magical concept, and it was used in many different forms. It was employed as an ingredient in several leechdoms and was thought to have a beneficial effect against 'worms'. Moreover, it was the common magical custom for a person to spit in order to remove evil.[50]

There are two chapters very near the end of the *Lacnunga*
which are worthy of some consideration. They are concerned
with the three days in the year when blood-letting should not
be performed.[51] These days, all three being Mondays, are
referred to as the Egyptian Days or 'dangerous days' when it
was unlucky for either a man or an animal to be bled. These
days were thought to be the last Monday in April, the first
Monday in August and the first Monday in January.

The *Lacnunga* warns that should a man or an animal be
bled on any of these three Mondays, then he will not live
longer than the first day after the blood-letting, or at the
longest the fourth day afterwards. Should he live longer than
this, however, he will certainly die by the seventh day!
Further, should the man take any medicine during these
three days, he will die within the following fifteen days, and
if anyone should happen to have the misfortune to be born
on one of these Mondays, he will end his life by an unpleasant death. The concluding sentence then goes on to
prohibit the eating of goose during the Egyptian Days for
otherwise the man will surely die within forty days. This
taboo on eating goose is of Celtic origin and it is therefore
possible that the beliefs in good and bad days for blood-
letting found in the Anglo-Saxon texts stem from Ireland.[52]

These are by no means the only times when bleeding was
considered to be dangerous during the Anglo-Saxon period.
As early as Bede's time, it was thought most unwise to perform venesection on certain days. He tells the story of Bishop
John of Beverley visiting a sick nun in the monastery of
Watton in Yorkshire. She had been bled in the arm and
apparently it had begun to swell, perhaps due to sepsis or
some deep bruising, and was causing the woman great pain.
John was asked to visit the nun; he inquired when she had
been bled and, on being told that the operation had been
performed on the fourth day of the moon, retorted angrily,
'You have acted foolishly and ignorantly to bleed her on the
fourth day of the moon. I remember how Archbishop
Theodore used to say that it is very dangerous to bleed a

patient when the moon is waxing and the ocean tide flowing.'[53]

Finally, contained in the text of the *Lacnunga* is an exceptional passage known as the *Lorica of Gildas*.[54] Loricas were special prayers intended to protect the body and soul from evil.

The *Lorica of Gildas* consists primarily of a long list of parts of the human anatomy, remarkably accurate for its time. Most parts of the body are mentioned, starting, as so often in the texts of this period, with the head and working downwards. Each part is separately listed so that it may benefit from the protection expected from the *Lorica*.

As far as the name Gildas is concerned, with which this lorica is associated, if this refers to the same person as the Celtic author of the well-known tract *De excidio Britanniae* then the text must be of quite an early date, for this Gildas died *c* 570. Whether or not this identity is accepted, there is certainly an Irish element in the *Lorica*; indeed, some sentences in corrupt Irish are included in the prayer.

In addition to this clue about its origins, the *Lorica* goes on to say '. . . have pity, so that neither the mortality of this year nor the vanity of the world may bring me down with it'.

The mortality or pestilence mentioned here was obviously the reason for the composition of the prayer, and must have referred to one of the many epidemics of pestilence from which the population of the British Isles suffered during the sixth and seventh centuries.

The *Lorica* was certainly written before the end of the seventh century, as Aldhelm, Bishop of Sherbourne, knew of it and he died in AD 709.

THE PERI-DIDAXEON

The name of this text means simply 'teachings' or perhaps 'medical doctrines' and it is of quite a different nature from the other treatises already discussed.

The erare sixty-six chapters, some of considerable length,

describing prescriptions and recipes in the style already noticed in the previous manuscripts; and they begin similarly with the head and proceed downwards. In this text, however, this descending scheme finishes with the hands. After these come remedies for such conditions as asthma, chest pain, acidity, vomiting and abdominal pains.

Here, in contrast to the *Leechbook* and the *Anglo-Saxon Herbal*, the prescriptions are generally much shorter and more simple and do not contain the great number of ingredients recommended in these other texts. The *Peri-Didaxeon* is a much later text and belongs to the twelfth century. It is an abstract of a Latin treatise attributed to the eleventh-century Petrocellus, while part of it is also thought to be the work of Gariopontus of similar date.[55] Two centuries separate the *Leechbook of Bald* from the *Peri-Didaxeon* and this may account for the latter's reputed greater degree of 'rational' material, although it has been shown that many passages are common to both texts.[56]

The manuscript begins with a potted history of medicine derived mainly from Galen. Instruments used by the god Apollo, such as '. . . the irons, when one healeth men with knives . . .' and the cupping glass are described, and an account is included of the doctrine of the four humours which was to become so common in later English and European practice.

After this follow the remedies for some of the conditions we have already discussed. Three typical examples are as follows:

For a broken head.
For a broken or wounded head which is caused by the humours of the head. Take betony and pound it and lay it on the wound and it will relieve all the pain.[57]

For sleep.
Thus must one do for the man who cannot sleep; take wormwood and rub it into wine or warm water and let the man drink it and soon it will be better with him.[58]

For sore hands.
This leechcraft is good for sore hands and for sore fingers which is called chilblains. Take white frankincense and silver cinders and brimstone and mingle together, then take oil and add it into this mixture, then warm the hands and smear them with the mixture thus made. Wrap up the hands in a linen cloth.[59]

A notable feature of the *Peri-Didaxeon* is that it contains many examples of Greek words translated into Old English, thus proving to some extent its Greek origin. Some of these are mis-spelt due, presumably, to the lack of acquaintance with Greek on the part of the Anglo-Saxon writer. Occasionally, Greek, Latin and French words are all contained in one leechdom.[60]

Taking this text as a whole, in spite of its more simple remedies, it is not a very weighty work either in length or content, and could not have been particularly useful to the physician. This is confirmed to some degree by the fact that only one manuscript of it still exists, suggesting that it may not have been known to many, nor in great demand.

MISCELLANEOUS LEECHDOMS

There now remains to be considered what one may well describe as a collection of odd remedies and charms, some having more of a veterinary significance rather than being intended specifically for human beings. These leechdoms have been taken from manuscripts, some of which were used later in book bindings and fly-leaves.

First, however, a brief word is necessary concerning a collection of texts contained in MS 17 St John's College, Oxford, and written *c* 1110.[61] It contains, amongst other subjects, sections on the four humours, blood-letting, prognostications, weights and measures, herbs, recipes for plasters and remedies for various diseases. While this text displays a wealth of medical knowledge, all the contents are typical of the medicine existing before the rise of the Salerno school and cannot therefore be assigned to it.[62]

To return to the miscellaneous leechdoms: there are, in addition, two larger passages of eleventh-century date deriving from Hippocrates. One of these concerns itself with the growth and development of the foetus[63] and the other deals with the methods by which it was considered that the sex of an unborn child could be determined.[64]

The first of these passages attempts to trace the process whereby the foetus develops and grows. There is little of gynaecological value or knowledge in it, except for the recognition, at the end of the chapter, of the dangers to the mother if the child is not delivered by the tenth month of pregnancy.

The nature of the second passage may be illustrated by its observation that if a pregnant woman should 'walk slowly and have hollow eyes, she will bear a boy; if she goes quickly and has swollen eyes, she will bear a girl'. Again, another method used to forecast the sex of a child is to take a lily and a rose and ask the mother-to-be to choose one of them: 'if she takes the lily, she will bear a boy, if she takes the rose, she will be delivered of a girl'.

A further prognostication is that if the pregnancy be of some four or five months' duration and the woman is fond of eating nuts and fresh fruit, then there is a likelihood of her having a mentally afflicted child. Moreover, a grave warning is also given that should the woman eat the meat of a bull, ram, boar, cock or gander, she exposes herself to the possibility of giving birth to a deformed child!

The fly-leaf leechdoms deal with an assortment of illnesses and diseases.[65] Leechdoms are suggested, amongst others, for vertigo, chest pain and eye troubles; and indeed one and the same prescription is recommended for two so diverse conditions as gout and wrist drop!

The charms which follow these remedies all deal with cattle and bees and do not immediately concern us.

From this survey of the medical textual material which was available to the Anglo-Saxon physician and, indeed, was used by Anglo-Norman practitioners also, it is clear that the whole concept and practice of medicine was a complex amalgam of herbalism, superstition, religion, folklore and empiricism. The effects of leechdoms and practices described in all these treatises cannot have been very beneficial by any standards. Some of the herbal mixtures and ointments may well have had some ameliorating properties, but it cannot be surprising that many of the sick and injured turned to the help and comfort offered by the Church and the miraculous intercession of the saints.

3

Religious Sources

For the many who did turn for help to their religion, its rituals and holy men, it was fortunate that they lived in a credulous age. Inexplicable events abounded and their easiest explanation was invariably that of divine intervention.

There was the almost universal belief, during the earlier centuries of Christianity, if not for much longer, in the power of working miracles, a power granted by God to His disciples and other holy men. Indeed, this very ability to effect the miraculous was regarded as proof of saintliness and deep piety. Extraordinary claims could never be tested and, to simple minds, any incident not immediately obvious or explicable must have been the work of God transmitted through His holy men. These, and in particular the saints, were as essential a part of the Old English religious world as they were of the whole of Christendom. The early Anglo-Saxons probably regarded them as a Christianised version of their recently discarded pagan gods.

During the entire Middle Ages, there was a ready acceptance of signs, wonders, miracles and the beneficial effects of holy relics even by the educated, let alone the mass of the peasantry. Shrines and tombs of the saints and the pious became centres of hope and comfort at a time when life contained little of either. To the medieval mind, these holy places became centres of pilgrimage where God's power was at its most beneficial and where cures for many ills, often treated unsuccessfully by physicians, could be sought.

The religious sources now to be examined for evidence of disease and illness and the methods, if any, which were re-commended for their cure, consist mainly of various *Lives* of the saints. It was perfectly natural at the time for the authors of the *Lives* to attribute all sorts of powers to their heroes: many of these were purely magical, such as quieting storms, making winds change direction or preventing the spread of fire; others, more relevant to us, were the profound belief not only in the ability of the saints to produce cures for the sick but in their possession of personal powers of healing. More-over, not only were the holy men regarded in such a light, but inanimate objects such as wood, water, wine, earth and clothing could be made a means of healing merely by their having had contact with the holy person. Much more effec-tive, however, were his personal possessions, but most holy and sacred of all, and therefore the most likely to prove beneficial, were the actual bodies and bones of these servants of God. This last belief permitted considerable exploitation of the superstitious mass of the population. Frequent frauds occurred, false relics were 'discovered' and miraculous events invented. This is not altogether surprising for as shrines earned a reputation for their curative powers, so would pilgrims flock in even greater numbers accompanied by their offerings. Some tombs even had holes cut into the coffin to permit the bones to be touched or objects inserted thus acquiring great virtues.

However slight the evidence for the miracles contained in the hagiographical literature about to be reviewed, or whatever the biblical origins of the healing stories, their authors can only have imparted medical detail which was known to them and therefore within the scope of contem-porary medical knowledge. These details can, not unreason-ably, be regarded as a fair reflection upon such medical thought and practice and, however fabulous or seemingly incredible some of the alleged cures appear, they can only contain medical evidence known to the writers at their particular time. It is true that medical details were frequently grafted on to biblical stories and legends but they would be brought up to date when substituting the saint concerned for the original character.

It should also be pointed out that when many of the miraculous cures are examined another substitution is found to occur: the replacing of older pagan customs and rites by Christian ceremonies. It is clear that the new elements were not always meant to supersede the earlier heathen remedies, but rather to enhance these with an aura of sanctity. Many cures are described in the religious literature, as indeed occur in the medical texts already noted, in which the pagan element is scarcely disguised.

Paganism long retained its influence after the Conversion and its persistence will be noted in other parts of this book, but for the moment it is clear that the ready acceptance of many healing miracles was made possible by the memory of the heathen past.

A further factor making for the easy acceptance of the miraculous cure was the kind of life experienced by the population, particularly in the earlier centuries of Anglo-Saxon England. Life was hard, uncomfortable and short, frequently punctuated by famine, pestilence and war. Any source of comfort would be unreservedly welcomed and if the new religion could provide assistance for the sick through the work of its holy men, the people would not be slow to accept its benefits.

In times of pestilence and epidemic, holy men went about their pastoral work consoling the afflicted and raising the spirits of those facing disaster. For instance, St Cuthbert, whose ministry will later be discussed in some detail, would travel far and wide about the bleak countryside where the population existed at the most primitive level. Such people tended to revert rapidly to paganism and the use of charms and amulets in their despair during periods of epidemic disease, as they did, for example, in Essex in 664. Cuthbert, along with other priests, moved around the villages at these times ardently preaching in order to revive any flagging in religious enthusiasm.[1] Most villagers, however, did not need convincing that these pious individuals possessed healing gifts, and would travel long distances for their advice and help when seeking cures for their complaints.

EPIDEMICS, 'PESTILENCE AND PLAGUE'

During the whole period covered by this book, countless epidemics are recorded in various parts of the country and it will be useful to discuss these briefly in relation to the lives and work of the saints. In the earlier centuries, the sixth and seventh, several widespread outbreaks of 'pestilence', 'mortality' and 'plague' occurred and their identification has given rise to much speculation. Itinerant Celtic missionaries have been suggested as the principal means by which the diseases were spread[2] and it is certainly true that monasteries suffered heavily from epidemics due to their enclosed form of life as well as their tradition of hospitality to visiting missionaries who could well have been carriers of disease. These diseases, whatever their nature, produced an impact sufficiently strong as to move Bede, even in his eulogy of Abbess Aethelthryth, to specifically refer to 'each frightful plague'.[3]

Bubonic plague, smallpox, dysentery and relapsing fever have all been suggested as causes of the periodic epidemics, but it is virtually certain that no one disease was the cause of all the outbreaks.

The very severe and widespread epidemic of 664 and the years following can serve as a good example of the difficulties to be faced when trying to determine its identity. Bede, in his *Ecclesiastical History*, describes how the epidemic began in the southern regions of the country, was followed by outbreaks in Northumbria, and even reached Ireland.[4] Both Bishop Tuda of Lindisfarne and St Cedd died of this pestilence in 664. Bede gives no further description of the disease nor does

he give any name to it. He himself narrowly missed con-
tracting it at this time, when all the monks at Jarrow had
succumbed.[5]

Cuthbert also fell ill with this disease while at the monastery
of Melrose and its prior, Boisil, died of it. Cuthbert recovered, 'but as the swelling which appeared in his thigh
gradually left the surface of his body, it sank into the inward
parts and, throughout almost the whole of his life, he continued to feel some inward pain . . .'.[6] Here Bede provides a
good description of a bubonic tumour, typically affecting the
glands in the groin; and as far as the 664 epidemic is concerned, it is certainly suggestive of bubonic plague. It is not
surprising that Cuthbert should fall victim to the illness as he
was constantly visiting villages during periods of pestilence.
On one occasion, he was in a village called *Medilwong* comforting the stricken inhabitants and, when he asked if anyone
was still suffering, a woman brought her dying son to him.
Cuthbert blessed and even kissed the child, who subsequently recovered.[7]

It has been suggested that this pestilence, like the great
epidemic of 545, was smallpox.[8] However, there is another
view that it was almost certainly bubonic plague.[9] The
former argument asserts that the black rat which must be
present as host before plague can spread did not appear in
England until about the twelfth to thirteenth centuries. The
second argument, on the other hand, remains convinced that
this outbreak of 664 was indeed bubonic plague;[10] for while
the rat may well be the most common carrier of plague, fleas
can also transmit the disease and, while less effective in
spreading it, the enormous number of fleas would compensate for any lack of rodent population.

The true identity of this 664 epidemic, like those which
broke out at various times in the succeeding centuries, will
remain uncertain. Many alternatives are possible and it is
fruitless to speculate, but in all likelihood, in addition to
bubonic plague and smallpox, which undoubtedly existed,
typhus, typhoid fever and dysentery at least would surely

have appeared periodically. Influenza certainly existed and a severe epidemic is known to have occurred about 1170. Furthermore, in view of the frequency with which paralysed youths appear in the literature, as well as those suffering from weakness of their limbs, it is not impossible that some infectious and paralysing disease such as poliomyelitis was responsible. Despite the unhistoricity of *Ingulf's History of Croyland Abbey*, it does contain a detailed description of a disease which could be considered typical of poliomyelitis. The author records that in 851 'a certain disease afflicted the whole of England; it was a kind of paralysis by which the nerves of men, women and children were attacked . . . the arms and hands, especially of men, became useless and were totally withered up, the attacks of the disease being preceded by an intolerable pain, which like an unerring forerunner, first took possession of the afflicted limb'.[11] The sequence of pain, paralysis and muscle wasting with deformity is very characteristic of this most infectious disease.

LIVES OF THE SAINTS AND BEDE'S ECCLESIASTICAL HISTORY

Bede, by far the richest source of evidence for miraculous cures and the healing powers of the early English saints, describes a large number of incidents in which to a greater or lesser degree medical details are either clearly apparent or may be reasonably deduced.

There is not the space to deal with all the relevant incidents and stories recorded by Bede, let alone those described by other authors, so it is intended to refer only to those which contain definite details of medical techniques or knowledge, or otherwise provide some illustration of the condition of early English medicine.

The principal English saints' *Lives* in which most of the examples of healing are described are the two *Lives* of St Cuthbert (died 687), one written anonymously at Lindisfarne between 699 and 704 and the other by Bede *c* 720 using

the earlier anonymous version as his guide.[12] Reference will
also be made to the *Life of Wilfrid* by Eddius, written a few
years after Wilfrid's death in 709,[13] and the *Life of St Guthlac*
by Felix, written *c* 730–40.[14] In addition to these, Bede's
Ecclesiastical History, written in 731, contains many examples
of healing and provides a considerable amount of incidental
medical detail.

It will be noted, however, that Bede and the other authors
were at pains to show that Christianity was as valid and
relevant as the previous heathenism and thus many of their
more extravagant claims must be viewed with caution. Notwithstanding this anxiety to press the claims of the new
religion and its saintly followers, Bede in particular does
inform his readers of his authorities, especially when writing
about the miracles attributed to Cuthbert. Though he was a
careful scholar and frequently claims eye-witness authority,
this is common hagiographical form and should not be
automatically accepted. It should be noticed, however, that
he does refrain from the more fabulous type of miracle.
There should also be borne in mind the ever-present tendency
for those clerics who were the source of many of Bede's
miraculous stories to be interested parties for the benefit of
their monastic houses or shrines.

Bede certainly accepted the veracity of the miracles about
which he writes, and of those concerning Cuthbert, for
example; though he takes as his chief authority the anonymous *Life*, he is not above enhancing some incidents to the
advantage of the saint. This can be seen when physicians
become involved, and examples will be given where, even if
a doctor could possibly have been successful, the saint is
nevertheless given the entire credit.

Many copies of biblical stories are recorded and are
entered into a saint's *Life* in order to increase his appearance
of sanctity and to perpetuate early Christian cults. These
will mostly be ignored as they do not normally illustrate
English medical traditions, but may be referred to in passing
in order to illustrate, or provide comparison for, other

incidents from which significant medical information can be extracted.

It is, of course, extremely difficult if not impossible to attempt to diagnose with precision the patient's condition or illness in most of the stories, because the authors of the various *Lives* were more concerned with the virtues, holiness and activities of the saint than in providing exact details of individual cases. The most that can be done is to try to discover how the diseases and ailments of the time were dealt with by both the physicians and the holy men. It is fully recognised that we may have to leave the realm of factual and secure evidence for that of speculation and supposition, but despite the difficulties involved in the medical interpretation of the miracle stories, the attempt seems worth making. The evidence is accepted as being imprecise, vague and perhaps even altered to suit the author's purposes, but it is still possible that medical information may be discovered from the recorded incidents.

A typical example among many of this vagueness of medical detail is the case recorded in both *Lives* of St Cuthbert of a certain servant called Sibba, described as suffering from 'a most evil disease'.[15] He was evidently near to death but was given water blessed by Cuthbert and, after sleeping deeply, awoke in apparent good health. It is impossible on the available evidence to advance any definite diagnosis, particularly as the removal of disease solely with holy water or blessed wine is a recurrent theme throughout hagiographical literature. One point, however, may be made: while the illness described in some cases does not appear in sufficient detail to make an identification, disease can change its character and symptoms. Hence, what might have been a reasonably clear description of a disease in the eighth century may be unfamiliar today.

A further group of incidents in which imprecision of symptoms makes identification impossible is that in which the patient is vexed by 'devils' or 'evil spirits'. For example, the wife of Hildmer, a royal official, was sick 'by a demon' and was so severely afflicted that she shouted aloud, gnashing her teeth and flinging her limbs about uncontrollably. Cuthbert was, nevertheless, able to prophesy her cure.[16]

Another person afflicted by a demon was a boy 'shouting and weeping and tearing his body'.[17] By this time, Cuthbert was no longer alive and the boy had been taken to various relics of martyrs without success. A priest, convinced that the boy would be helped by the intercession of Cuthbert, dissolved in water a particle of earth which had soaked up the water which had washed the saint's body. This was given to the patient, who was soon cured of his madness. Two points may be made about this case. The posthumous power of Cuthbert was made out to be more beneficial than the other martyrs appealed to, and secondly, while it was the association with Cuthbert which give the earth its significance in the eyes of the priest, from the patient's point of view, what may have mattered most was the Germanic pagan tradition that earth possessed magical healing powers.[18] On the other hand, virtually any object associated with a saint would be regarded as possessing healing properties, whether or not the object, coincidentally, had a pagan significance.

In both these cases we may be dealing with outbursts of insanity if we accept the evidence at face value, though perhaps an epileptic type of seizure is more likely in view of the fact that in so many cases 'demon possession' ends after a long deep sleep.

Attacks of pagan frenzy cannot be ruled out. The age of the Conversion was a time of great psychological upheaval for the simple-minded peasants, and so-called 'devil vexation' could have indicated some acute form of mental distress resulting from the recent loss of familiar, and no doubt comforting, pagan beliefs. In the *Life of Guthlac*, a young man 'attacked by an evil spirit' injures himself in a frenzy 'with wood and iron, with his nails and his teeth'.[19] For a heathen, iron had long been credited with magical properties which could have been the reason behind the author specifying this

material. An interesting incidental point in this case is that
although the youth had previously killed three men with an
axe, he was untypically allowed to remain unbound at home
with his parents.

A case worth noting because it represents an eye-witness
account of an instant cure is that in which Cuthbert healed
a sick boy while travelling from Hexham to Carlisle. He
came across a group of women bringing a youth 'wasted
with a long and grievous sickness' to be blessed by him. He
asked the women to leave and gave the boy his blessing
'which drove away the disease' even though, we are told,
physicians had previously, though unsuccessfully tried their
medicines. 'Thereupon the youth rose . . . received food and
was strengthened and returned to the women who had
carried him.'[20] The implication that the boy was able to
walk at once is clear. As wasting and atrophy are common to
many diseases, they do not help in identification. The youth
may have been weak simply because he was recuperating
from a previous, though not mentioned illness. Malnutrition
is another possibility, particularly as Cuthbert was then in
an upland district where food would be scarce, and it is
significant that there is a specific reference to the boy having
been given food. Further, in corroboration, Bede's account
clearly records the incident as having occurred in 'a moun-
tainous and wild region', a district unlikely to have been
especially fertile. Pulmonary tuberculosis could have been
responsible for the wasting and weakness, but in the final
analysis, the identity of the disease must remain uncertain. It
is unfortunate that we are told nothing of the boy's subsequent health in view of the instant nature of his recovery, but
in other cases some evidence is available which suggests that
cures were not always permanent. There is, for instance, the
reference to Bishop Winfrith's deacon whose infirmity was
healed twice by Cuthbert's relics, implying a relapse after the
first cure,[21] though in fairness to the memory of the saint, it
is not known how long the period was between the two episodes of illness. The health of the entire population at this

time was greatly at risk and even if one complaint was helped
by a saint or his relics, the patient could well have suffered
later from another sickness, though a recurrence of an
illness would not have been unusual.

A noteworthy case where a saint certainly effected a permanent cure is that of Guthlac's help to Ofa who had a
thorn imbedded in his foot. Ofa's legs became swollen, his
joints were inflamed and he suffered a high temperature. He
was brought to Guthlac, who wrapped him in his own sheepskin rug, whereupon the thorn came away and Ofa recovered,
it is said, within the hour.[22] There is no suggestion that
Guthlac extracted the thorn himself, although this possibility
naturally exists and the warmth from being covered with the
sheepskin can only have been beneficial to Ofa's general
condition. The sheepskin had special significance to those
present as it was used by the saint when at prayer. It is not
known how long the accident had occurred before the visit
to Guthlac, but in view of the lack of evidence of previous
treatment for what must have been a common hazard, the
case displays a serious lack of medical sense among the local
population, let alone by any leeches in the district. Indeed,
it is almost certain that if Ofa had been given treatment by a
physician, the author, as we have already seen, would have
been only too willing to record it in order to advance Guthlac's subsequent cure. Ofa, it would seem, suffered from a
severe degree of cellulitis, if not septicaemia, but whatever
the actual condition, he survived the episode for some thirty
years to witness charters into the 740s.

A further permanent cure is that concerning Abbess
Aelfflaed of Whitby, daughter of King Oswiu of Northumbria. During the lifetime of Cuthbert she had long suffered
from a serious illness, at one time being very near to death.
Her physicians could do little for her, though in time a
partial recovery did take place. The internal pain had left
her but, as her limbs remained weak, she could not stand
upright nor move about except on all fours. She suddenly
thought that if only she could possess something which

belonged to Cuthbert she would certainly be restored to health. Shortly afterwards, Cuthbert sent her a linen girdle to wear and within three days she had fully recovered her strength.[23] Aelfflaed actively survived her illness for at least twenty-nine years, dying in 716 at the age of sixty, and for this reason was not likely to have suffered from any serious disorder such as a severe stroke or cerebral haemorrhage.

A similar miracle occurred after Cuthbert's death, again making use of items of clothing. A paralysed youth is said to have been transferred from his own monastery to that at Lindisfarne in order to be treated by the more skilled physicians there. These doctors tried every possible cure for his powerless limbs but finally despaired of him. The boy then asked for the shoes which had belonged to Cuthbert who had died long before. He had them put on his feet and went to sleep; when he awoke he had regained the use of his limbs.[24]

In both this case and that of Aelfflaed, the cures obtained were regarded as having been due solely to the virtues of objects belonging to the saint. The paralytic youth himself described how the paralysis developed and he is quoted in the anonymous *Life* as saying, 'This powerlessness and mortification first began from my feet and so spread through all my members.' As the condition began in the feet, so the reason for requesting shoes becomes apparent. He could have suffered, therefore, from an ascending paralysis of the kind seen in an infective polyneuritis in which a group of nerves become inflamed leading to muscle weakness and paralysis. This may possibly be supported by the fact that it is not unknown for polyneuritis sufferers to recover spontaneously. In this particular case, recovery could have been occurring at the very time the patient requested the shoes.

In Aelfflaed's case, absolute faith in the girdle, hence a most determined resolve to get well, could account for her continued recovery. The wearing of the girdle would provide just that extra psychological stimulus to encourage her to straighten up and walk which had been considered impossible before. Furthermore, she would almost certainly have been encouraged by her recognition of the similarity between Cuthbert's girdle and St Paul's aprons and handkerchiefs being used to heal the sick (Acts 19: 12). A mild hemiplegia or stroke could have been responsible for her paralysis, or more simply, suffering from the debilitating effects of a long period of illness which she is said to have endured. In either case, firm resolve due to her absolute faith in the power of the girdle could have been sufficient to encourage her to move.

As far as the time factor is concerned, in both the case of the paralysed youth's recovery overnight, and of Aelfflaed's in three days, there has been considerable contraction for dramatic effect with typical hagiographical licence.

A similar story, though this time concerning St Guthlac, is worth noting here and it is quite likely that it is based upon Bede's account of Aelfflaed's recovery. A warrior named Ecga was suffering from an 'unclean spirit' and although he had retained strength in his body and limbs, his speech and understanding were lost. He was taken to Guthlac who wrapped his belt around Ecga who was soon restored to normal behaviour. The warrior thereafter always wore the belt and, apparently, had no further trouble.[25]

An interesting feature of the healing work of the saints was that just occasionally neither they nor the sick person necessarily expected a cure to follow any blessings bestowed. For instance, a certain nobleman, Hemma, whose wife was seriously ill, asked Cuthbert to bless some water so that she might be quickly healed or, if she was to die, to do so the more easily.[26] Similarly, a member of Bishop Willibrord's household prayed at Cuthbert's tomb to be granted either restoration to full health or quick death.[27]

St Wilfrid is given credit for an uncommon kind of miracle. A nun had suffered from a withered arm and deformed hand for many years. She bathed her arm in water which had just been used to wash the cloak in which the saint's body had been wrapped. The nun 'plunged it into

the warm soapy water and rubbed it with the cloak'; soon
the use of the whole arm was restored.[28] While the recovery
is naturally attributed to the cloak's healing power, it is just
possible that here is another instance of faith overcoming a
handicap, particularly as warm water is often helpful in
making movement easier; a simple form of hydrotherapy.

Various stories are told in the *Lives* where, as has already
been suggested, the curative powers of the saints are exaggerated whenever reference is made to the work of physicians. In many cases the physicians are totally unable to help
the patient until subsequently the holy man succeeds. In one
case, however, it is unclear whether a physician did effect a
cure or whether this was indeed the holy work of Bishop
John of Beverley. A youth from near Hexham suffered from
'so much scabbiness and scurf on his head that no hair
could grow on the crown save for a few rough hairs . . .'. The
bishop, after blessing the boy, called in a physician to
attend to him. Later, the youth's skin healed and grew 'a
beautiful head of hair'.[29] If the boy had suffered from a
psoriatic condition, no doubt the doctor could have bathed
the scalp and applied a salve of helenium in butter, soot,
salt, tar and honey;[30] the tar and honey conceivably being
of some value for this disorder. The point remains, of course,
that the boy's improvement was regarded as being solely due
to St John's blessings.

This case raises the question of others in which the
alleged miracles could have a purely natural explanation.
For example, in the case just described, as well as the scalp
disorder the youth also suffered from aphasia or loss of
speech. He was certainly not deaf, for St John practised
speech therapy with him, beginning with the letters of the
alphabet and then progressing to normal speech. John is said
to have accomplished this task in only a day and a night, but
this could again be a contraction of time made for effect.

A further case of a possible natural cure is one in which a
blind man, believing he would see if only he could touch an
object which had been blessed by St Guthlac, was cured by

water in which a previously blessed piece of salt had been dissolved.[31] Several points of interest arise here. The man is said to have gradually lost his sight over a period of twelve months until finally his eyes became covered with 'yellowish clouds of film' and could not distinguish day from night. Ointments and fomentations had been unsuccessfully applied, but now, as the blessed salt water was dropped into his eyes, the cloudiness cleared and sight was restored. A definite diagnosis seems impossible but some form of cataract or membranous film would seem to have been responsible for the gradual loss of vision. Salt water, in such a case, may have been beneficial by helping to wash and disperse the opaque film, but whether such a treatment was of help or not, saline was widely regarded during this period as a remedy for several eye conditions;[32] while saline irrigation is still today a standard eye treatment. Once again, however, as far as the blind man was concerned, the power of salt lay in its association with the saint.

Perhaps one of the most interesting of the healing narratives concerning the earlier saints is one in which Cuthbert himself was the victim. It is also a case where a perfectly normal treatment could have been successful even though the saint's piety and holiness were, of course, given the credit. The story is particularly noteworthy in that not only are a number of symptoms supplied in both the anonymous *Life* and Bede's *Life*, but rare corroboration is possible due to Cuthbert's remains having been scientifically examined at the end of the nineteenth century.

Cuthbert as a young man was afflicted with what the anonymous author describes as a piercing and painful swelling of the knee, and Bede as a sudden and piercing tumour of the knee.[33] Both writers record that the sinews contracted, the foot of the affected leg could hardly touch the ground and walking became almost impossible. A passing stranger, whom Cuthbert took to be an angel, advised him to apply a mixture of hot wheaten flour and milk to his knee, after which the joint improved.

There are several observations which can be made about this story. Firstly, the anonymous author states specifically that no doctor had examined Cuthbert's knee, yet Bede disagrees for he quotes Cuthbert as saying that 'no doctor with all his care can heal me'.

If a swelling shows at the front of the knee, it is more usual to hold the joint in the straight or extended position in order to reduce any tension or stretching of the swelling; thus, in Cuthbert's case, if his knee was bent and contracted, it is much more likely that the swelling was situated behind the joint. This is confirmed by Bede's reference to the swelling as being *in poplite*, that is, in the popliteal space at the back of the knee. Therefore any suggestion that he could have been suffering from synovitis or water on the knee[34] is, on balance, unacceptable for the reason already pointed out, that such a swelling is unlikely to cause flexion, but rather extension of the knee. Moreover, one of the most likely causes of synovitis in the knee is injury and there is no evidence that Cuthbert had previously fallen victim to a blow or fall.

As the question of pain, in addition to swelling, features prominently in both versions of the story, some sort of abscess becomes a possibility; indeed, an acute abscess would be both rapid and painful as both authors suggest. Bursitis is another possibility, particularly involving one of the bursae lying near to the back of the knee. On the other hand, however, swelling of any of these and perhaps particularly of the *semimembranosus* bursa, a condition very often found in young people, is unlikely to be very painful or large, and produces little if any contraction of the tendons. The degree of pain implied in the narrative would suggest, therefore, that the most probable cause of Cuthbert's painful and swollen knee was an acute form of abscess.

There has been another suggestion that the saint may have suffered from some tubercular condition,[35] but even if this was the case, and the suppurating ulcer on his foot[36] and the extensive and chronic ulcerative condition found on his

F

sternum and clavicle could possibly point to this diagnosis, it cannot be blamed for the swollen knee. An untreated tubercular knee joint would almost certainly become functionally disorganised and it is difficult to imagine it possible for Cuthbert to have continued his active life, frequently travelling long distances, over many years with such a disability. Furthermore, of much greater significance is the fact that when Cuthbert's skeleton was examined in 1899, an irregularity found on the head of the right tibia, which might have suggested a tubercular condition, was in fact *post-mortem* change due to natural bone decay.[37] Finally, if this knee condition had been due to a tubercular cause or, indeed, any serious bone disease, the remedy suggested by the angel would have been quite useless, but for an abscess (or perhaps simple bursitis) it would have served admirably as a hot poultice. What is especially worth noting in this case is that whether or not a physician had seen Cuthbert's knee, the fact that such a simple remedy had not previously been suggested by anyone illustrates again the very low level of medical knowledge prevailing in seventh-century village communities, though there is no doubt that similar hot poultices were frequently prescribed in later medical texts.

A final example of a probable natural cure given the benefit of divine authority comes from the activities of St Columba of Iona. On this occasion a young man came to Columba complaining of frequent nose bleeding, whereupon the saint 'pressing together both his nostrils with two fingers of the right hand' soon stopped the haemorrhage.[38] There is no further evidence to indicate that this was any more than simple digital pressure to the nose in order to arrest the bleeding.

In all the cases so far described, the miraculous healing has been through the activities of saints and other pious men. There are examples, however, of cures being effected by secular persons though, of course, they were highly regarded for their piety. King Edward the Confessor, for instance, is said to have been instrumental in restoring sight

to several blind men, and in both his *Life*, written by a monk
of St Bertin in 1067, and in William of Malmesbury's
Chronicle of the Kings of England, he is credited with two cures
worthy of further mention.

The first concerns a young married woman who not only
was unable to bear a child but suffered from an infection of
her neck glands, probably scrofula or the King's Evil, which
became swollen and disfiguring. She dreamed that she would
be cured if King Edward would wash her neck. When the
king heard of this, he gave his consent and with his fingers he
washed the affected areas several times, making the sign of
the cross. Due to the pressure of his hands, pus and blood
flowed out from the various holes which had appeared from
the separation of the good from the diseased skin. Soon
afterwards, healthy new skin grew and covered the scars and
the woman was not only completely restored to health, but
within a year gave birth to twins.[39] William of Malmesbury
further records the interesting observation that though the
power of curing the King's Evil was thought a special attribute of royalty, Edward nevertheless cured this disease while
in exile in Normandy before he ascended the throne.
Therefore William considered that this power was granted to
Edward by virtue of his great piety rather than hereditary
kingship.[40]

To King Edward was also attributed the restoration of
sight to a blind man who had previously visited no less than
eighty churches and their shrines. The man, named Wulfwin, had become blind after heavy labour felling trees with
'the blood stagnating about the eyes' and, after nineteen
years of blindness, was persuaded in a dream to visit these
churches to pray for a cure. He eventually reached Edward's
court at Windsor where the king heard of the dream and
agreed to help. He dipped his fingers into water and placed
his hand upon the man, whereupon Wulfwin regained his
sight and was subsequently given a responsible post at court.
Furthermore, this same water, later administered by servants, was also successful in curing four other blind men.[41]

Several other miraculous cures were performed by Edward the Confessor, including cases of quartan fever and a monk who had suffered from tumours on his arms and legs.[42]

By no means were all miraculous cures confined to the Anglo-Saxon era and before passing on to the healing activities of Anglo-Saxon holy men, Wulfstan, Bishop of Worcester, provides an interesting link between the two periods. He was appointed bishop in 1062 and died in 1095 and his *Life* was written by Coleman, his chaplain for many years. It is this *Life* which William of Malmesbury used as the basis for the only surviving version, written between 1124 and 1143.[43] Wulfstan is credited with curing several cases of frenzy and insanity, though no diagnostic detail is provided. They do show, however, that physical restraint was still regarded as the normal means of dealing with the mentally sick.

The prayers and blessings of Wulfstan are said to have cured other illnesses but insufficient information is available to allow even speculation as to their identity. Only in one case is something more than vague generalities recorded. A poor man from Kent suffered from the 'King's Evil' or tubercular glands, though later he is regarded as a leper, which may well have been the correct diagnosis for the man appears to have been 'so poisoned in all his members . . . that he went about as a living corpse. He was horrible to behold, for he was running with foul matter, horrible to hear, for his speech was a kind of hoarse whining.' Water used by Bishop Wulfstan was poured into the sick man's bath and he immersed himself, 'his flesh full of sores'. After the bath his skin and flesh improved and even the sores on his head disappeared and his hair grew again.[44] The ulcerating tissues, the hoarse or raucous voice, the mass of sores and loss of hair all suggest true leprosy, though the remedy seems to be totally inadequate without some divine intervention.

ANGLO-NORMAN SAINTS

The first post-Conquest religious source to be reviewed is the *Life of St Anselm*, written by Eadmer, a constant companion of the Archbishop of Canterbury from 1093 until Anselm's death in 1109.

A detailed incident of a miraculous cure is one in which a knight called Humphrey suffered from dropsy, severe enough for him to have been given up by his doctors. He had known Anselm personally and often used his name when praying for God's help. A Canterbury monk came to visit him, bringing a belt which had belonged to Anselm. When 'he saw the sick man with his whole body so blown out with this disease that all who saw him thought he would burst', he gave the belt to Humphrey, who kissed it and wrapped it round his body, though its ends would not meet due to his distension. The swelling then began to subside and the ends of the belt began to overlap. Each limb reduced in size as the belt was moved over it until recovery was complete. Humphrey was then given a strip cut from the belt, which he used successfully when a recurrence of the dropsy occurred some time later.[45]

The main part of the belt, now in the care of Eadmer, was used to cure an Englishwoman suffering from a serious illness while living in Scotland; he was, at this time (1120), Bishop of St Andrews. The lady was quite content to die in the company of Christ, but consented to have Anselm's belt wrapped around her. After a few days she recovered and Eadmer specifically states that this cure took place in his presence.[46]

Eadmer used Anselm's belt again, when he returned to Canterbury in 1122, on a monk dying of a fever. When he placed it around the sick man's neck, the fever soon abated and the monk made a speedy recovery.[47]

After Eadmer has described several other cures using Anselm's belt, he significantly emphasises that such events

are not incredible for 'such things can be done by so great a
man standing in the presence of God . . .'.[48] People believed
sincerely that their religious fathers could dispel disease and
readily regarded as supernatural many everyday activities.
Furthermore, as they were for ever on the watch for the
slightest suggestion of divine activity, it was easy to be so
convinced.

There is, of course, an obvious similarity between these
stories and that concerning St Cuthbert's girdle and Abbess
Aelfflaed,[49] which is but one example of similar events being
repeated in various saints' *Lives*.

Before Anselm's death, even scraps of food from his table
were believed to have healing properties against fevers and
similar illnesses. Two knights sick with quartan fever and
stomach pains were cured by eating such crumbs of food.[50]
A similar story is told of a seriously ill nobleman who, after
being given some bread blessed by Anselm, soon recovered.[51]

A characteristic feature of several holy men was their
curious aversion to food which became regarded as a sign of
special piety, even where the refusal was due to ill health
rather than from any spiritual austerity.

After Anselm had been ill for some time, food became
distasteful to him. Realising he could not live without eating
he would take a little food, but nevertheless he slowly
weakened. He fully recognised his danger, for he said,
'Truly I think I might recover if I could eat something . . .
I am enfeebled by the weakness of my stomach which refuses
food.'[52]

Likewise, in the last years of Ailred, the Abbot of Rievaulx,
his refusal to eat led to severe emaciation, and he went
farther and positively refused even his medicines. In referring to Ailred's treatment, Walter Daniel, his biographer,
who lived under the abbot's rule for seventeen years, says
that, 'During this period he rejected the curatives which he
had been wont to take, and if by chance he tasted anything
of that kind in his mouth, he took it out with his fingers . . .
threw it on the ground and ground it to powder with his

foot . . .'[53] Here is an almost certain indication that medicine in tablet form was available in the mid-twelfth century. Ailred's austerity went as far as to dilute the wine specially prescribed by his physicians as being most helpful in his illness.

Ailred seems to have been an invalid for much of his life and his sufferings occupy a prominent place in his *Life*. The considerable detail provided would suggest that Walter Daniel was present during these bouts of illness, which included attacks of arthritis, rheumatism, gallstones, dysentery and, finally, some serious bronchial disorder. His arthritis became so painful that he was carried about on a linen sheet and his general condition was such that he was permitted to sleep and eat in the infirmary and given several other important privileges.[54]

The fever from which the Sub-Prior of Revesby suffered is said to have been cured by Ailred. Walter Daniel's graphic eye-witness account of the prior's symptoms includes difficulty in breathing and

His frame was so wretchedly wasted that it looked like the hollowed woodwork of a lute; eyes, face, hands, arms, feet, shins, blotched and misshapen, proclaimed that the death agony was nearer and nearer . . . So the sick man lay upon his bed, his limbs scarcely holding together, for the contraction and loosening of his joints and nerves made them leap from the sockets of his bones and only a thin layer of fragile skin kept his body together . . .[55]

The prior, on being told by Ailred to go to church and pray, was soon after restored to health and was able to continue his work.

Another monk of Revesby, a skilled craftsman, was cured with the help of Ailred's staff. The monk had sustained so severe an injury to his arm that 'it was threefold twisted back upon itself like a ram's horn'. One day he saw the abbot's staff in church and, taking it in his good hand, passed it round his injured arm three times while making the sign of the cross. 'At the third movement and the third life giving sign, his arm immediately shot back to its normal place, his hand resumed its natural mobility . . .'[56] This case is suggestive of a dislocated shoulder being successfully reduced by the rotary movements necessary to wield the staff and make the sign of the cross.

A case in which medical detail is given, though difficult to analyse, is that of a monk ill with a stomach complaint, serious enough for the physicians to show their concern. The patient was speechless while the 'humours' had gathered together accompanied by severe stomach pains. Ailred had merely to place his forefinger on the patient's mouth and ask him 'to speak in the name of the Lord' for a full recovery to take place.[57] A similar command to speak and a touch on the lips was sufficient for Ailred to cure a shepherd who had been dumb for three days.[58]

Walter Daniel provides another eye-witness account of the illness of a monk with heart failure. He was unable to see, hear or speak and was nearing his end. His limbs were paralysed and he was reduced to laboured breathing through the nose. By the time Ailred reached him, his pulse had ceased; thereupon the abbot brought several relics of saints and the text of St John's Gospel and bound them all to the monk's chest, praying that the patient be cured. Immediately afterwards the monk made a full recovery.[59]

Perhaps the most detailed symptomatic account in Ailred's *Life* is that of his own terminal illness. Walter goes to great pains to describe his master's appearance and symptoms during the last year of his life. In addition to the previously mentioned ailments, Ailred was now troubled by a dry cough and frequently lay exhausted on his bed. He suffered also from a fever 'which starting from the brain, affected the sockets of his eyes, forehead and every part of his head and was so great that he could not endure for an instant, because of the pain, the weight of anything placed upon him, from the crown of his head to his extremities'. His tongue was sore, throat ulcerated, mouth hot and dry and he suffered from thirst. He died in 1167, aged fifty-seven, succumbing after many days without food.[60] Apart from the probability of some chest and lung disorder, an attempt to suggest a specific diagnosis of Ailred's final illness is clearly impossible.

More may be said, however, in a case where Bishop Hugh of Lincoln assisted a young man from Rochester. This youth, being unable to resist his physical desires, admitted to many sins. Now, full of contrition, he wished to save himself. Hugh, hearing the story, told the youth to follow him to Canterbury and with prayer and advice he was able to resist further temptation. However,

> Suddenly the flesh round both his thigh bones and privy parts gangrened and two holes, or rather caverns of a terrible size and depth appeared and yet he felt no pain at all from these immense wounds. For fear that they might become worse, he showed these putrid sores to a very devout man and a skilled healer of wounds, Master Reginald Baker, who told us that his rotting flesh had fallen away almost to the bowels.

Hugh soon healed the youth by applying warm candlewax to the wounds.[61]

From these details it is not unreasonable to assume that it was sexual activity in which the young man had indulged. He admits as much himself, for he says, 'At first however, and indeed almost every time I sinned I was led astray by the persuasion of another person,' thus suggesting that venereal disease may have been responsible for the ulcers, particularly as his 'privy parts' were mainly involved. The physician, Reginald Baker, in spite of his alleged piety, either did not bother to treat the youth or did so without success.

It is possible that the size of the ulcers have been exaggerated and warm wax applied could well assist in the circulation, granulation and healing of the sores. On the other hand, if a gangrenous process was indeed present, then it is difficult to see how any simple remedy would have sufficed.

The mentally sick were still bound and physically re-
strained, even in St Hugh's time (*d* 1200). On one occasion,
while he was visiting the village of Cheshunt, a group of
villagers implored him to bless one of their neighbours possessed by a demon. Inside his house, the victim was lying
bound with his head, hands and feet tied to large stakes in
the ground. The wretched man repeatedly gnashed his
teeth, rolled his eyes and stuck out his tongue. Hugh comforted him by reciting St John's Gospel, and blessed him
with water and salt, some of which was put into his mouth.
From then on the man regained his senses and later spent
much time in pilgrimages.[62] Whether this was a case of acute
insanity or perhaps epilepsy is not clear, but severe restriction of movement was evidently still imposed as in earlier
centuries.

After Hugh's death, a blind woman claimed her sight
restored after touching the saint's body and the local people
asked for the bells to be rung in recognition of a miracle.
Hugh's biographer, Adam of Eynsham, argued against this,
as he was unsure whether the woman had pretended blindness. He was clearly aware of such frauds, for he goes on to
say, 'It is essential carefully to ascertain the truth about this
and other miracles which assuredly be reported and not have
any proclaimed or published unless they were confirmed.'[63]
Such a critical approach to supposed miraculous events must
surely be rare for the beginning of the thirteenth century,
even though, nearly a century earlier, Eadmer expresses
concern at the ready acceptance of uncertain miracles.[64]

Of all the English saints and holy men, the one who has by
far the most numerous healing miracles attributed to him is
St Thomas of Canterbury. Almost from the moment of his
death in 1170, miracles were reported in ever-increasing
numbers. His tomb rapidly became the favoured shrine for
countless pilgrims suffering from an endless variety of
diseases and disabilities. The political climate of the time,
coupled with Thomas' pious stand against Henry II, made
martyrdom almost a certainty and, in consequence, equally

certain was the expectation of miraculous events by the credulous population.

Cures for every conceivable kind of affliction, handicap, disease and mishap were claimed to result from an appeal to Thomas' shrine or, alternatively, by the taking of a mixture of his blood in water. The miraculous effects of Becket's constantly diluted blood were made available over a wide area of the country, due to its being contained in conveniently carried tin or lead phials. Blindness, insanity, leprosy, drowning, haemorrhage, lameness, deafness, dumbness and even malignant tumours are just a few of the great variety of disorders claimed as cured or at least much improved by those who took themselves to Canterbury. Moreover, it was not always necessary to visit Thomas' tomb personally, for miraculous cures were reported as far afield as the Welsh border where relics of the martyr had been deposited in Cheshire and at Exeter where a vision of Thomas was sufficient to arrest an outbreak of influenza.[65]

It is impossible here to attempt even a passing review of any individual cases from the many hundreds recorded, but what should be noted is that Benedict, the monk who acted as guardian of Becket's tomb, took it as one of his main tasks to inquire into the many alleged cures. Such pains did he take over his investigations that pilgrims are reported as having been much upset and annoyed by his persistence. However, he seems to have been more than willing to accept all but the most fabulous claims, as was his brother monk William who shared the guardianship of the shrine.

In conclusion, it should be restated and emphasised what has already been stressed. It should not be readily nor automatically assumed that the supposed healing miracles detailed in this chapter were all the product of a credulous and simple-minded clergy, engaged in some far-fetched hero-worship of their religious fathers. Merely because it is not possible to determine now how much truth is contained in the stories, either from vagueness or inherent improbability, they should not be spurned and entirely dismissed. It is quite probable that a kernel of accurate information has been transmitted, even if there has been much exaggeration of the saints' beneficent activities. However absurd or incredible some events may appear to a modern sophisticated society, it should be remembered that the people involved in the incidents lived in an age of great faith, hope and convinced expectation of help from their saintly leaders. Perhaps also the therapeutic and psychological stimuli engendered by the saints and their relics cannot now be fully appreciated, but in the cold hard world of the Middle Ages such apparently supernatural acts would not only be readily accepted at their face value, but would be confidently received with unquestioned belief.

4
The Physician and His Treatment

It should be said at the outset that positive evidence which
might throw some light upon the person and character of the
Anglo-Saxon leech is very limited, obscure and vague. His
position in society, for example, is hard to determine; the
views of his patients, or indeed his colleagues can be but
dimly perceived; and the social and professional position of
the medical profession in general is similarly lacking in
detail. None the less, by piecing together scraps of information which may, in the main, be of an incidental kind, some
picture can emerge from the rather shadowy world of the
Anglo-Saxon medical practitioner. It is regrettable that we
know so much less about our native physicians of this period
than we do about their continental colleagues, whose lives,
status, work and character are so much better documented.
On the other hand, however, we are fortunate in having the
considerable volume of medical material available which
enables us to study exactly how the leeches went about their
craft and how they attempted to deal with the medical
problems of their time.

To the Anglo-Saxon, the physician was known as the
leech, or in Old English, the *laece*, and it is important to
remember that he was not at all concerned with the treatment of specific diseases or illnesses but confined himself to
the application of a multitude of botanical, animal, reli-

gious, superstitious and other remedies to an equally numerous collection of symptoms. Pathological processes were virtually unknown to him, as was any conception of disease causation and physiological function in general. In addition to his trying to deal with this host of symptoms, he had to face the ever-present medical problems of his time stemming from the effects of famine, plague, pestilence and violence.

Some indication of the leech's appearance, or at least a contemporary artist's impression of his appearance, is suggested by several illustrations in which he is portrayed at his work.[1] There is no indication that he wore the clerical tonsure; he is seen both shaven and bearded and is clothed in the normal dress of the period. There is no suggestion, either, of the leech wearing any distinctive medical dress as was to be the trend in later centuries. These details would suggest that, in addition to the monastic physician, who would almost certainly be a monk and whose activities were mostly, though not entirely, restricted to the monasteries, there was a body of lay medical practitioners who were available to offer their services to those members of the population able to afford them.

We have already seen in chapter 2 the texts and treatises from which the leech prescribed his remedies in the normal course of his duties and, when examining the contents of these manuals, it is necessary to appreciate, as was stressed earlier, that very many of the prescriptions and recipes recommended would have been quite impossible to prepare. Indeed, many of those which could conceivably have been made up would have been more unpleasant to take than the effects of the disease.

The existence of these various leechbooks containing so much advice over a wide range of medical practice raises the important question of whether any sort of training or preparation was available for those interested in following a career in leechcraft.

There is evidence, though circumstantial and scanty,

which suggests that there was some form of medical education offered to the budding leech, even though it is clear that he was required to learn his subject uncritically and mechanically direct from his texts. Furthermore, he was not encouraged to question his material but rather to accept what he saw and read; while his acquaintance with the practical side of his work was almost entirely academic. Examination of the patient was virtually unknown and the leech merely attempted to treat only that which he could see or could deduce from the patient's obvious symptoms. Notwithstanding these limitations and his overdependence upon earlier Classical authorities such as Galen, Aristotle, Dioscorides, Hippocrates and others, he did venture outside their medical concepts on various important matters.

In the *Leechbook of Bald*, there are phrases which indicate that some form of instruction was available. In the first leechbook there are several phrases, such as, 'Some teach us . . .'; 'Leeches who were wisest, have taught . . .; 'Leeches teach that no man . . .'; and, 'Oxa taught us this leechdom . . .'[2] In this latter case, for example, the leechdom was for 'the dry disease'. In the second leechbook there is a further example of a name being included and an indication of some tuition. 'Dun taught it . . .' and in this instance the teaching was a remedy for 'lung disease'.[3] While it may be thought that these phrases could just as well refer to the ancient physicians from whom the leech took much of his material, there can be no doubt that the inclusion of names like Oxa and Dun suggests a contemporary Anglo-Saxon origin. The names of these two leeches, together with those of Bald, Cynefrith and possibly Cild, are the only Anglo-Saxon physicians known to us. Cynefrith, incidentally, though described by Bede as a *medicus* or physician, was clearly also a surgeon. It is very doubtful if these two branches of medicine had separated at such an early date, for he practised *c* 680 and is the earliest recorded Anglo-Saxon physician.[4] In the last years of the Anglo-Saxon state, the identities of other physicians have been established, but these were mainly members of the clergy originating from Normandy and France. The outstanding example is Baldwin, Abbot of St Edmund's Bury. His medical skill was well known and in 1059 he became physician to Edward the Confessor. He remained at Bury for many years and was retained as physician to William the Conqueror when he succeeded to the English throne.

Indications that the study of medicine was included in more general schemes of study during the pre-Conquest period, even if not yet as an independent discipline, come from other and non-medical sources. Bede's story about Bishop John of Beverley criticising the action of a physician in not bleeding a nun in the manner in which Archbishop Theodore had taught is but one example.[5] This would suggest that Theodore had at least some medical knowledge which he imparted to his students, although there is no evidence that he personally practised the craft.

It is quite possible, however, that even if there was a superficial, formalised kind of medical training, many would-be leeches would have learned their skills on a trial and error basis or as apprentices or assistants to practising physicians. This could well have been a satisfactory method of training in view of the type of treatment expected of the leech. In fact, in the early twelfth century, it is quite certain that some sort of apprenticeship existed, for William of Malmesbury refers to John of Villula, Bishop of Wells, in 1100, as 'an approved physician, by practice rather than education'.[6]

An even more haphazard basis for training was evidently not considered unworthy when occasion demanded. King Magnus the Good, for instance, after the battle of Lyrskop Heath in 1043, did not have enough doctors in his army to attend to all the casualties. He immediately went round his soldiers and picked out those whose hands he considered best suited to medical work, those 'who had the softest hands and told them to bind the wounds of the people, and although none of them had ever tried it before, they all became after-

Page 101 *Surgery for epilepsy (12th–13th century)*

Page 102 (far left)
*Cautery points,
including those for
toothache and dropsy
(12th century);
(left) a physician
preparing cautery irons
(11th century)*

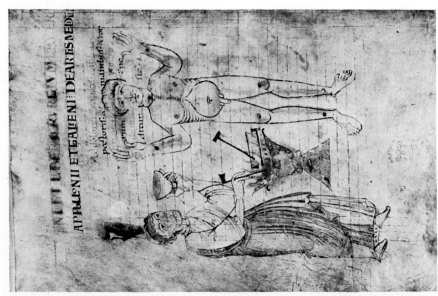

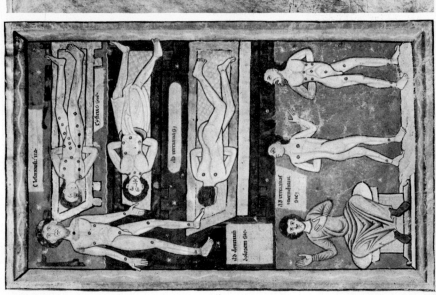

wards the best of doctors'.[7] Indeed, so successful were two of these untutored physicians that they founded medical dynasties, for we are told that from them 'many good doctors are descended'.[8]

That the leech was at least literate in his own language is obvious from the use he made of his texts, but whether his standard in Latin was the equal of that of his colleagues in the monasteries is doubtful. Nevertheless, even without Latin, he would be able to attend to his patients as well as the medical knowledge of the times permitted for, as we have seen, most of his instructional material was fortunately available in Old English.

Leeches must have formed a sort of loose group of professional people who were by no means necessarily ecclesiastics, for there is no doubt that although monasteries possessed their own physicians, they certainly used the services of lay practitioners on occasion. Similarly, monastic physicians are recorded as having attended to the needs of patients living in nearby districts. An interesting example of a monastery calling upon the services of a lay physician is the story concerning Cynefrith who, as will be described in the next chapter, operated upon St Aethelthryth. He must have given satisfactory service to the Abbey of Ely as Bede implies that he visited and practised there for at least sixteen years. It is doubtful that he was a monk because he was not among the monastic community at the time of the exhumation of Aethelthryth's remains, but was 'called in' to see the body.[9] It is possible that even if he was a monastic physician, he may not have been regarded as a 'full' member of the community but thought of rather as a retainer and would therefore have had to be 'called in' on such a solemn occasion.

As a professional body, leeches, it is only to be expected, would charge fees for services rendered; and this was indeed the case. This is verified by the Old English word *laece-feoh* or leech fee. Moreover, in his *Life of St Wulfstan*, written early in the twelfth century, William of Malmesbury specifically refers to the 'hiring' of physicians and to the fact that

G

people could well have 'spent most of their substance' on physicians' fees.[10] The story concerning Abbot Baldwin also confirms the charging of fees. The Bishop of Thetford, Arfast, having been injured in the eye by a thorn and being in great pain, was advised to consult Baldwin, even though there was no love lost between them. Baldwin agreed to treat him but only after the payment of a fee!

The ethical standards of the leech are difficult to establish with any certainty. Scanty information does exist but, as might be expected, it is of a contradictory and conflicting nature. The earlier sources, such as Bede and the various *Lives* of the saints, give the impression that physicians did try their best to help their patients. That these *Lives* also contain many examples of their lack of success is understandably due to the need to enhance the subsequent miraculous cures performed by the saint. Indeed, this emphasis on failure could not be otherwise as the work of the physician was invariably overshadowed by that of the priest due to the fact that most, if not all, of the early sources stem from the clerical pen. However, even in failure, the impression persists that the leeches worked hard for their patients and gave them what comfort was within their power and competence.

There is a remarkable absence of criticism at their lack of success in the earlier literature. It might be expected that some adverse comments would have survived regarding what must have been the frequent failure of the leech. In spite of his large collection of herbal remedies, superstitious practices and remedies of animal origin, much illness and disease must have taken its course. King Alfred is a noteworthy instance where even important and high-born individuals could not be cured of long-standing afflictions.[11] Bishop Aethelwold, an important prelate and a colleague of St Dunstan, also suffered from a prolonged disease of his bowels and similarly was unable to find a cure. There are many further examples of comparable lack of success and inability to cure illness, yet there is no real evidence of criticism directed against the physician, nor can any censorious attitudes be discerned in the sources. Perhaps this charitable acquiescence was due to the fact that illness was a general and frequent feature in Anglo-Saxon society and there was no real expectation of relief. Should a cure be established, this would be something of an exception. It was noted in chapter 1 that the population suffered from a very low average age at death and it is probable that there was much fatalistic acceptance of illness as just another part of their hard physical existence. Another reason for this curious lack of complaint could possibly stem from the fact that leeches must have been relatively few in number and could only have been patronised or retained by the more wealthy section of the population. The number of patients personally attended by each could never have been very large and the mass of the population would have had to cope with whatever advice reached them, probably through several hands, from the leech retained by the local land-owner or thegn. In this way, village folk medicine was established and practised by and for the local village communities.

The other and more critical side of the picture can be seen best from the later literature. In the *Life of St Wulfstan*, physicians are not credited with much sense of ethical duty. In the example already quoted of people spending 'most of their substance' on physicians' fees, the leech seemed quite unmoved when the patient's family were brought face to face with bankruptcy due to the amount of his fees. In the same *Life* there is a story of a crippled woman whose husband 'sought such aid as they could afford from physicians'. Worse is to follow: 'the physicians did their best and plied their craft and what they could not do, they made up in promises – but all their consultations were to no purpose.'[12]

John of Salisbury, the famous courtier and man of letters, also had no great opinion of his contemporary physicians for he considered that 'they have only two maxims which they never violate, "Never mind the poor, never refuse money from the rich." '

The impression left by all this evidence, flimsy though it may be, is that standards of professional and ethical conduct had shown a decline from those observed in the earlier centuries. There is the further suggestion that as the medical practitioners gradually formed themselves into an organised professional and mainly lay body, moral considerations were allowed to deteriorate as concern with financial considerations increased.[13] In slight mitigation, however, there is little doubt that leeches incurred professional expenses and even had bad debts, for in a *Penitential*, Bede mentions that payment due to a physician could be postponed for up to a year.[14]

Before any detailed consideration can be given to the treatments offered by the Anglo-Saxon practitioners, several preliminary observations should be made.

It has already been pointed out that, except for the animal recipes in the *Medicina de Quadrupedibus*, medical treatment was virtually limited to medicines, salves, ointments and plasters, all having a predominantly botanical origin. The medicines intended for oral use were usually prepared by dissolving the required herbs, sometimes after boiling and pounding, into ale, beer, oil, honey or vinegar.

The leech had to work within the limitations of whatever materials happened to be available and one of his real difficulties must have been, as has already been noted in chapter 2, that many of the remedies given in his leechbooks were to be prepared from ingredients not readily available to him. It becomes quite obvious from even a cursory glance at the medical texts that any evidence of clinical observation by the physician is extremely rare. His remedies were fixed and did not vary with his patient's progress and if one prescription was unsuccessful, he very often had several others to try, but any physical examination of the patient seems to have been sadly lacking. None the less, some ideas of internal physiology must gradually have circulated, even if they were only vaguely appreciated. When William the Conqueror, for example, had sustained the injury from which he was subsequently to die, his physicians forecast certain death after examining his urine. Possibly they saw evidence of blood which could indicate some serious internal injury. In any case, examination of the urine seems to have been one of the few diagnostic methods adopted by the late Saxon and Norman physicians and various illustrations portray the physician carrying his urine flask.[15]

On the other hand, at least one example exists where there is not only acute observation concerning the cause of disease but also an attempt at differential diagnosis. This involves a case of stroke or hemiplegia. Bald's second leechbook warns:

> The disease comes on a man after forty or fifty winters . . . if it happens to a younger man, then it is easier to cure, and it is not the same disease, though unwise leeches consider that it is the same half-dead disease. How can a like disease come on a man in youth in one limb as the half-dead disease does in old age? It is not the half-dead disease, but some mischievous humour is placed on the limb on which the harm settles; but it is easier to cure and the true half-dead disease comes after fifty years.[16]

Is there not just a hint of medical controversy here? Notice also the view that a man of forty or fifty is regarded as being 'in old age'.

Perhaps physicians carried on some sort of professional discussion or debate among themselves and there is no reason to think that they never carried out tests or simple experiments. In fact, in 1116, King Siward of Norway, though not himself a physician, certainly performed medical experiments. In order to save his men from dying in large numbers while in Constantinople, he made them dilute their wine. This he found to help their illness, 'for pouring wine on the liver of a hog and finding that it dissolved by the acridity of the liquor, he conjectured that the same effect took place in men and afterwards dissecting a dead body, he had ocular proof of it'.[17] This observation speaks volumes for the quality of medieval wine! If a non-medical person could so experiment, it must surely indicate that physicians might be expected to be able, even anxious, to carry out simple experimentation.

The leech had little acquaintance with internal disease; it was with the outside or exterior of the body that he mainly concerned himself. This is not surprising considering the social conditions of the time, when many disorders would show themselves on the skin and other superficial tissues. The low standard of personal hygiene, for instance, would have had a markedly adverse effect upon general health and many of its results would become apparent on the external organs such as the skin, eyes, hair and teeth. In addition, changes in skin colour and tissue swelling or wasting might also become obvious. The number of recipes for the eradication of lice, fleas and other vermin indicates just how much of a nuisance was this single aspect of low hygienic standards. Moreover, various skin disorders would have been common due to malnutrition, vitamin deficiency and lowered vitality and for these conditions also many prescriptions are recommended in the leechbooks.

Despite the handicaps due to his lack of understanding, the leech did possess some knowledge of prognosis, even in the earlier periods. Bede describes the case of a young man who developed a progressive swelling on his eyelid. The leeches attending him had applied poultices and ointments without success and, as a last resort, some advised that it be lanced. Others strongly disagreed, fearing complications.[18] The suggestion here is that experience had taught at least some of the physicians that precautions were necessary in certain procedures in order not to make matters worse. Nevertheless, there are examples in the *Leechbook of Bald* and elsewhere of ludicrous prognostic methods. A patient's fate would depend upon the direction in which his face was turned at the time he was visited by the leech, or reliance was placed upon various complicated lunar calculations.[19]

A further handicap with which the leech had to contend was the absence of a real concept of quantities or weights and measures for the preparation of his prescriptions. At first there seems to have been no accurate measurements and vague phrases are used such as 'a handful', 'a moderate quantity', 'an eggshell full' and even the use of 'the thumb and forefinger', although most prescriptions do not give even these indications of quantity. Gradually, more exact weights and measures came to be adopted and references to coins are given to indicate weight.[20] Eventually a detailed table of weights was drawn up in the last chapter of Bald's second leechbook.[21]

It seems certain that the experienced leech could not only identify many of the herbs he required but would also have tried to grow some of those more commonly used. Herb gardens became common in the monasteries, and no doubt the lay physician also had his source of supply. In the second leechbook for example, there is a clear indication of herbal qualities as well as the recognition that the effectiveness of a remedy may vary with its strength.

A wort drink [an enema]; choose scammamy thus, break it in two, put a bit on the tongue, if it bursts out white as milk then it is good . . . if it [the medicine] be good the dose will be one pennyweight; if moderately good, one and a half or two pennyweights; if bad, three; no more than that.[22]

Various prayers and charms were frequently offered at the gathering and preparation of the herbs, many of which may have been substitutions for earlier pagan invocations, while prayers to the apostles, paternosters and holy signs were all commonly adopted in the belief that these would increase the beneficial effects of the medicines.[23]

MAGIC AND SUPERSTITION IN MEDICINE

The physician, both in the earlier centuries of our period and, to a lesser extent, later, treated his patients not only with material medicines and natural practices but, to a considerable degree, supported these with supernatural and magical rites and influences. Many of these rites were intended for the patient's own use.

The employment of amulets and other objects regarded as possessing magical significance, incantations, prayers and charms were all part of a leech's practice and are frequently encountered in his treatises. All these superstitious rites stem primarily from the Anglo-Saxon concept of disease causation. While certain Latin medical texts contained such superstitious factors and so became incorporated into early English medicine (see chapter 2), the main stream of magical medicine is the product of native Saxon or Teutonic concepts brought by the migrating tribes from their homelands and subsequently developed. As Christianity spread throughout the country, a leavening of Christian rites and prayers was added to existing heathen magic and both existed side by side for many years and, in fact, as will be seen later, there are examples where both elements are contained in one prescription.

The persistence of pagan influences in general, and not only in medicine, is well attested by the enactment of several laws found necessary over many centuries and, indeed, up to the thirteenth century and after, to curb these supernatural practices.[24] It is, therefore, only to be expected that in man's concern for such a fundamental instinct as self preservation, half-forgotten folklore and heathen traditions should surface and retain a hold upon his basic beliefs. One of the many revealing examples of this is Bede's story in the *Life of St Cuthbert*. During an epidemic of plague, many people 'profaned the faith they held by wicked deeds and some of them . . . forgetting the sacred mystery of the faith . . . took to the delusive cures of idolatry, as though by incantations or amulets or any other mysteries of devilish art, they could ward off a blow sent by God the creator'.[25]

There can be little doubt that ancient heathen beliefs and practices long remained a significant force among the general population of Anglo-Saxon and Norman England. At times they must have exercised through men's subconscious a certain influence on their thoughts and actions and so became directly involved in the creation of folk medicine and similar forms of primitive healing.

The Anglo-Saxon concepts of disease causation from which arose much of their superstitious medicine originated in the Germanic homeland and can be clearly distinguished from the many other elements in Anglo-Saxon medicine. There are three principal and basic concepts which are characteristic of this early native origin. The first is the belief that disease is the result of *elfshot* in which elves throw 'darts' which produce pain and disease. The second concept is that of the *worm* in which it was thought that a wormlike creature was responsible for much illness and the third of these original Germanic concepts was that both illness and its cure could involve the number *nine* in some way. Any leechdom, prescription or invocation containing any of these beliefs is proof of the existence, or at least the lingering traditions, of old Teutonic magic.

To ensure a degree of rationalisation and the limitation of evidence to a reasonably modest length, this study of superstitious medicine must be confined to the principal groups or characteristics and will provide only, and very briefly, examples which occur in the more widely used texts.

There are six main groups of prescriptions which provide evidence of superstition and magic in early English medicine and these will be arranged, for convenience, in the order compiled by J. F. Payne.[26] These recipes or prescriptions are those which

1   involve the use of prayers, invocations and incantations employed in the picking and the preparation of the herbal medicines,

2   use prayers and other religious rites over the patient, or are written down and used as amulets and charms applied to specific parts of the body,

3   use the powers of exorcism to expel evil spirits,

4   adapt narrative charms concerning legendary people

supposed to have suffered from a similar disease to that of the patient,

5 use material magic where certain objects such as stones, plants and animals are employed, not as medicines themselves but as sacred objects or personal charms,

6 involve the concept of disease transference by which certain ceremonies and rites were performed aimed at removing the disease from the patient to the object of the invocation, eg to an animal, object or frequently into running water.

Prayers in the gathering and preparation of herbs
Bald's first leechbook contains a fine example of this type of charm when it advises that to prevent travel weariness, mugwort should be used either held in the hand or held in the shoe. When plucking the plant, the traveller must say: 'I will take you artemisia [mugwort] lest I weary on the way.' The sign of the cross is made as the plant is pulled from the earth. A similar aid to travelling is contained in the *Anglo-Saxon Herbal*, also referring to mugwort.[27]

In the *Lacnunga*, the plant celandine is prescribed for haemorrhoids and when it is pulled up, nine paternosters are to be recited. Here the inclusion of *nines* suggests that the Christian prayers have been substituted for an earlier heathen invocation.[28]

Examples occur where objects are made beneficial by prayers and other similar verbal rites. In the *Lacnunga* there is a remedy for pain around the heart in which water from a spring, collected by a virgin, should have the Creed and a paternoster said over it. She is to collect water for nine days to achieve full benefit. Here are both *nines* and running water (transference), indicating pagan origins with the Christian elements added.

Spoken and written charms
Amulets and charms worn about the body were a frequent device to ward off disease or reduce its ill-effects. Their use

is frequently encountered throughout the medical texts. One example using virtually meaningless jargon written down on paper was to be hung from the neck as a cure for diarrhoea;[29] while another has some religious words written down and again the charm is to be hung from the neck to protect the wearer from 'dwarfs' or small malignant beings.[30]

There is an interesting mixture of Christian and heathen elements in the rite to be observed when protecting oneself from the 'evil rune lay' (a heathen charm). Greek words are to be written down with the intention of invoking the help of Christ. This charm shows an appeal to Christ used as a weapon against the pagan concept of rune lays, which suggests belief in both Christianity and paganism, in that there is simultaneous acceptance of the power of both the evil runes and their opposing amulet or charm within the same paragraph.[31]

Belief in the power of the spoken word is demonstrated in the first leechbook which prescribes an antidote for adder bite. All that is required is for the single word *Faul* to be pronounced.[32] Against the bite of a viper a long prayer to St John is advised,[33] and as a protection from typhus, a mixture of prayers and ancient heathen runes are to be recited.[34]

Exorcisms

A glimpse of this type of charm is contained in the first leechbook where exorcism for the fever is described. Holy water and prayers are combined to drive out the evil spirits.[35] A similar exorcism, but for the mentally sick, requires the taking of holy water with the singing of twelve masses in honour of the apostles.[36] The priest as well as the leech often took part in exorcism; Bede mentions how a priest was called in when a man was suffering from a violent fit. 'The priest pronounced exorcisms and did all he could to soothe the madness.' In this case, however, the priest was unsuccessful.[37]

Narrative charms

These usually invoked legendary figures and charms of this kind have persisted into modern times.

For a charm against 'the stitch, draw a Cross and sing three times this over the place with a Paternoster: Longinus, the soldier pierced our Lord with a lance and the blood stopped and the pain ceased'.[38]

A long narrative charm to counter the hostile 'dwarfs' is contained in the *Lacnunga*,[39] and a most comprehensive one against toothache runs:

> Christ sat upon a rock, Peter stood sad before Him, holding hand to jaw and the Lord asked him saying, 'Why art thou sad, Peter?' Peter answered and said, 'Lord, my teeth hurt'. And the Lord said, 'I adjure thee, O megrim or malignant drop [migraine or painful spot], by the Father and Son and the Holy Ghost, and by heaven and earth and by the twenty orders of angels, and by the twelve apostles, and by the four evangelists, and by all the saints, who have been pleasing to God from the beginning of the World, that the devil may not be able to injure him the servant of God, neither in teeth nor in ears nor in palate, nor break his bones nor gnaw his flesh; that thou mayest have no power to harm him, sleeping or waking, nor mayest touch him for sixty years and one day' Amen.[40]

Material magic

There are many instances of superstition where objects, animals and plants are all used as amulets and sacred objects considered to possess protective powers against disease.

A child suffering from epilepsy was thought to be helped by drawing a goat's brain through a golden ring.[41] A gold ring, used with the plant knotgrass, was also prescribed for sore eyes.[42]

Sometimes the amulet was required to be placed near to, or directly upon, the affected part. For stomach ache, the heels of a hare were to be placed on the clothing near to the stomach; and for swollen eyes, the eyes of a crab had to be placed upon the neck.[43] In cases of fever, the right foot of a dog was to be hung from the patient's arm.[44]

A remarkable example of a non-personal type of material charm is one where a badger's liver is carried around the boundaries of a man's land, and the walls of his town, after which the heart is to be hidden at the gates of the town. All disease will, in consequence, be driven away from the town and the man will remain in good health.[45]

To carry a canine tooth of a fox extracted while the animal was still alive was regarded as beneficial in cases of leg inflammation.[46] Animal teeth generally were popular as amulets as can be seen from the considerable number recovered from burial sites. Teeth and various kinds of shell, sometimes pierced in order to be worn as necklaces or bracelets, were considered to be of valuable assistance in childbirth and these also have been found in large numbers.

Strings of beads, often of amber, were widely used as a protection against disease and danger, for this material was regarded as possessing great virtue. Amulets made from plants were also frequently used and betony, vervain, peony, yarrow, mugwort and plantain were all very popular. Betony was the most highly esteemed plant for this purpose, while peony was also much favoured and remained so up to recent times.

A further example of a material charm, this time recommended for headache, is to lay crosswort on red cloth and bind it on to the head.[47] The red colour raises the suspicion of a pagan origin. Red was Thor's colour and was the colour associated with success and triumph over evil and disease. Red is found in several prescriptions: for instance clovewort wrapped in red thread, placed around the neck in April or October, would calm a lunatic.[48] For the protection of one's premises from devilish influences, it is advised that a red plant be attached to the doors of the house, further indicating the powers attributed to this colour against the forces of darkness and evil.[49]

Disease transference
This group of superstitions and magical aids in medical

treatment was the result of the widely held belief that disease could be transferred from the victim to some object or animal which could then be disposed of. Running water was frequently used for this purpose, in order, so it was thought, to carry away the disease in its current.

Certain skin disorders were treated with a herbal ointment while the patient's neck was scarified and the blood allowed to flow into running water. The patient had to spit three times, saying: 'Have this evil and depart with it.'[50] This prescription displays another magical feature, that of spitting. Saliva was used in many forms of magic and was thought to counteract the malign effects of 'worms and serpents'. It also formed an ingredient of several prescriptions for joint pain and eye diseases.[51] The actual act of spitting was also popularly regarded as removing the presence of evil; and closely associated with spitting was the practice of breathing or blowing upon wounds or painful areas. Blowing may well have been regarded as beneficial in removing evil,[52] and as the Germanic peoples considered that breath contained man's vital force, its use in any attempts at reducing pain or healing wounds can be readily appreciated.

In order to counteract the effects of 'flying venom' (airborne infection), a piece of oak was used to strike the patient until blood was drawn. The wood was then thrown away while he sang a religious verse or spell.[53]

In some inflammatory conditions, the patient's name was to be carved into a stick of hazel or elder. Three scratches were made over the affected part and the blood from these allowed to fill the spaces made by the carved name. The stick was then to be thrown over the patient's shoulder or between his legs into running water.[54]

In concluding this brief account of Old English superstitious medicine, it should be noted that various other charms were used, though perhaps less frequently. There are some which involve the use and repetition of numbers,[55] and one answering an urgent plea for peace and quiet advises on how to prevent a woman's chatter! 'Take a radish after fasting for the night and that day the chatter cannot harm you.'[56]

Runes were occasionally used as charms. Some of these ancient Nordic inscriptions, frequently seen on memorial stones and the like, were regarded as possessing healing properties and there were accepted health runes just as there were birth runes, battle runes and victory runes.

Another group of superstitions were those involving taboos. These were often concerned with various prohibitions in order to avoid bad luck, but could also take the form of positive commands intended to increase the beneficial effect of the treatment.

Iron and other metals are several times encountered as having magical properties. In Bald's second leechbook there is a suggestion of the alleged virtues of iron. Similarly, in the *Anglo-Saxon Herbal* there is a recommendation that when 'sea holly' is dug up, its roots should be detached with 'a hard iron'.[57] The prohibitions on iron, on the other hand, are met more frequently. For those afflicted with a neck tumour, several plants are required but none must be gathered by the use of an iron tool and this same taboo is repeated in the prescriptions for haemorrhoids and for the removal of the effects of 'elfshot' and also when mandrake is to be gathered.[58]

Silence or a taboo against noise was employed in the treatment of certain inflammatory conditions; similarly, when treating various skin disorders, silence was to be observed while the patient's neck was scarified and the blood allowed to flow into running water.[59]

Another superstition was that regarding the left and right sides. Should a man or animal swallow 'a worm', a song was to be sung into the right ear; should the 'worm' be female, however, then the song was to be directed into the left ear.[60] This charm was also recognised as an exorcism, for singing into the ear would drive out the evil spirit. To defeat the 'dwarf', a charm was to be sung first into the left and then into the right ear.[61] Only the left thumb and ring finger (the leech finger) were required to take a mulberry from its tree in a case of 'flux of the blood', while in cases of pain and prickling of the eyes, if the right eye was affected, then the right eye of a hound was to be bandaged on to it, and likewise for the left eye.[62]

Finally, the use of earth should be noted. Earth was the subject of worship going back into the mists of antiquity and has long had healing properties attributed to it, virtues which have persisted in some areas to the present day. For 'water elf disease' (dropsy?), for example, the following song is recommended: 'May earth bear on thee with all her might and main.'[63]

MISCELLANEOUS TREATMENTS

Any attempt in the space available to deal with the innumerable treatments offered by the leeches for the bewildering variety of illness and disease that was encountered must be severely curtailed and selective. Only a short account can therefore be given of the treatments recommended for the more common conditions which, though not always clearly identified, were probably those most frequently seen by the physician.

One of the principal groups of afflictions which required the attention of the Anglo-Saxon leech must have been those affecting the eyes. There are more leechdoms or treatments suggested for these conditions than for any other single complaint. The prevalence of eye disease and discomfort was, no doubt, due to two main factors. Firstly, the diet consumed by the people would have been the cause of much ocular ill health; vitamin A deficiency and periodic absence of fresh vegetables could give rise to such conditions. Moreover, the general lack of hygiene, both personal and domestic, would surely result in eye complaints. For instance, the practice of positioning the hearth in the middle of the villagers' cottages would be the cause of much smoke escaping into the living area with constant irritation of the eyes.

Page 119 (above) *A sick lady with her physician – the dropped urine flask indicates that the case is hopeless;* (below) *the patient has died and a* post-mortem *is in progress (13th century)*

turn→

Page 120   (above) *A physician attending to women patients and dispensing medicine;* (below) *the physician on horseback taking leave of his patients (13th century)*

In addition, the close proximity of animals which sheltered in the cottages could not only have had a deleterious effect upon general health, but could well have been a cause of many eye disorders.

Most of the medical texts contain remedies for eye diseases and their treatment involves the use of many different medicines. In the first and third books of the *Leechbook of Bald*, there are no fewer than twenty-three sections devoted to recipes for such eye conditions as 'mistiness', 'eye ache', 'white spot', 'pearl' (cataract?) and styes.

For 'mistiness' of the eyes, several herbs are prescribed, some mixed with balsam, honey, rainwater, sea-water or wine, to be either smeared on to the eyes or used to bathe them. Some of the remedies are more than usually difficult to understand. In one recipe, salt mixed with honey is to be applied to the eye. One can only presume very little salt was used, well diluted in the honey! In the *Lacnunga*, there is a prescription for an eye-wash made by mixing wine and pepper, and an even more uncomfortable treatment is that for 'unsharpsighted eyes'. This shortsightedness was expected to be improved by applying a salve made from pepper, salt and wine.[64] Nevertheless, salt was evidently considered beneficial in non-medical literature. In both the *Life of St Guthlac* and the *Life of St Columba*, for example, salt previously blessed by these saints was used to cure eye disorders.[65]

Pain in the eyes, cataracts, styes, swellings and other complaints all have their remedies based upon various herbs mixed in wine, water or honey. An eye salve in powder form can be made from 'beetlenut' and sulphur, burnt salt and pepper mixed together and kept dry in an animal skin. 'Introduce a small amount into the eyes with a toothpick; afterwards let him rest and sleep, and then wash his eyes with clean water and let him keep his eyes open under the water.'[66]

The *Lacnunga* prescribes several eye remedies: for example, 'the best eye salve' is a mixture of honey, fox's grease and roebuck's marrow. For a stye or boil: 'Take marrow soap

H

and hind's milk. Mix together. Let it stand until it is clear.
Take the clear liquid and put into the eyes. With God's help
the boil shall disappear.' 'For watering of the eyes, take
green rue and soak with honey, wring through a linen cloth
and put into the eye as long as need be.'[67]

In the *Peri-Didaxeon*, a prescription for a stye mixes barley
meal with honey to be applied to the eye, or alternatively
bean meal mixed with soap could be used.[68]

A survey of the *Anglo-Saxon Herbal* soon reveals that certain
herbs were considered to be of particular value in the treatment of eye complaints. Betony, southernwood, rue, wood
lettuce and celandine are amongst those most frequently
used. Indeed, betony was held in such high esteem in the
Middle Ages that an Italian proverb advises, 'Sell your coat
and buy betony' and a Spanish phrase was 'He has as many
virtues as betony'.

Another group of diseases which feature prominently are
those concerning gynaecological disorders. These would be
relatively common due to the rigours of childbirth, the untreated complications which would undoubtedly follow it
and the heavy physical stress under which women lived. The
Anglo-Saxon Herbal contains many prescriptions for female
disorders, while the *Medicina de Quadrupedibus*, *Lacnunga* and
the first and third leechbooks of Bald also contain several
remedies.

Miscarriage apparently proved something of a problem
for there are several recommendations specifically aimed at
its unfortunate results. The *Anglo-Saxon Herbal* advises the use
of dittany in the case of 'dead born offspring'. If the mother
is suffering from a fever it is to be taken in water, otherwise
in wine.[69]

The *Medicina de Quadrupedibus* recommends a hare's dry
heart rubbed to dust, added to frankincense and taken in
wine for seven days as an antidote for spontaneous abortion
and if this occurs frequently, the woman is strongly advised
to drink this mixture for thirty days. Should it prove necessary to expel a dead foetus, wolf's milk mixed with wine and

honey is to be given. The third leechbook prescribes brook-lime and pulegium boiled in milk and water and drunk twice daily for the same purpose.[70] This same chapter prescribes brooklime or hollyhock boiled in ale and taken hot as a means of expelling the placenta.

A most remarkable example of a superstitious charm used to avoid miscarriage states:

> Let her go the grave of a dead man, and step three times over the grave, and say three times these words,
>> Be this my aid against hateful slow birth;
>> Be this my aid against monstrous birth;
>> Be this my aid against hateful misbirth.
> And when the woman is with child and she goes to her lord to bed, then let her say:
>> Up I go, over thee I step,
>> With a living child, not with a dying one,
>> With a full time one, not with a doomed one.

The intention here is for the woman first to bury her misfortune in the ground, then, when pregnant again, to reverse the charm by stepping over a living person.[71]

Soreness of the breasts must have been a common ailment too. Cannabis mixed with grease (fat) and applied to the swollen breasts is one recipe; another is to drink wine containing the berries of the gladden plant; a third is to mix butter with knotgrass, to be applied to the part.[72]

To assist in maintaining regularity of monthly periods, women were advised to drink iris dust dissolved in vinegar; or shepherd's purse was prescribed.[73] A more rational treatment for late or irregular periods is that contained in the third leechbook. The woman is to be given a hot bath after taking a herbal drink and a poultice made from beer dregs, green mugwort and barley meal is to be applied to her genital region.[74]

Should a woman wish to conceive, the *Medicina de Quadrupedibus* recommends an amulet made from a bone 'found in a hart's heart, sometimes in its belly; hang that bone on a woman's arm and tie tightly, she will conceive'.[75]

Sexual disharmony is obviously not only a modern problem. The first leechbook warns that if a man be too lustful, 'boil water agrimony in foreign ale, let him drink it at night fasting. However, if he should be too bashful in such matters, then he should boil the same plant in milk for this "gives him courage".'[76]

Even if herbal drinks were regarded as beneficial in sexual difficulties, the sexual act itself was not exempt from being advised in certain cases. In 1114, the dying Thomas, Archbishop of York, was told by his medical advisers that recovery was impossible 'except by means of carnal knowledge of a woman'. His anguished reply came: 'Shame upon a malady which requires sensuality for its cure!' and he chose to die in virgin purity.[77] On the other hand, accepting similar advice did not guarantee recovery. Caesarius of Heisterbach tells of a critically ill priest who was advised by his doctor that unless he consorted with a woman, he would not regain his health. He did as he was advised but, nevertheless, died shortly afterwards.[78]

Vapour baths, both herbal and steam, were taken and some were prepared by either placing heated stones in water or pouring water on to a large heated stone, the patient sitting in the resulting steam. Sufferers from such conditions as 'heartache', leg fractures, jaundice and chest pain are all recommended to take these baths.[79] One example of a vapour bath is of particular interest. In the treatment of 'blotch', thought to be a skin disease, a number of herbs including betony, agrimony, yarrow, mint, fennel and dill were boiled and kept hot. A stool with a hole in its seat was placed over a bucket. The patient sat on the stool while the hot herbal liquid was poured into the bucket beneath and a garment was placed over him to prevent the vapours escaping.[80] A similar vapour treatment with stool and bucket was more rationally prescribed for what is most probably a case of anal fistula or, possibly, haemorrhoids.[81]

To conclude this survey of the treatments recommended by leeches for their patients in Anglo-Saxon and early

Norman England, here is a brief and fragmentary review of the more interesting advice and prescriptions offered to the patient.

Wine was a common ingredient in many herbal medicines and was used, no doubt, to give a more palatable taste to what must have frequently been very nasty, bitter and unpleasant concoctions. Moreover, wine itself was long regarded as a valuable medicine and prescribed freely. Ailred, the great Abbot of Rievaulx, was recommended by his physicians to take wine in order to overcome his illness but resorted to baths to assist the passage of bladder or kidney stone, a condition from which he is long said to have suffered. Indeed, his biographer indicates that so acute was his condition on occasion that Ailred made no less than forty visits to the bath hoping this would soften the obstruction.[82] The first leechbook, however, suggests the drinking of saxifragia and parsley boiled in ale as beneficial for bladder stone.[83]

Medicines in the form of pills and lozenges were known and used as an alternative to liquids. Ailred, as noted in chapter 3, even when seriously ill, would take no medicine and when his brethren tried to help by putting pills secretly into his food, would refuse them.[84] Another religious figure, Christina of Markyate, a hermit devoted to prayer, was sent by a well-wisher a tablet which, when dissolved in wine, was reputed to have cured her malady. In a vision, Christina was also given a lozenge-shaped tablet containing medicine.[85]

Balsam was a popular medicine and we have seen that Patriarch Elias of Jerusalem highly recommended it to King Alfred for the cough and 'for all infirmities'. It was used medicinally in the monasteries; both Ailred and Anselm are known to have kept supplies of it.

That dysentery due to deficient hygienic standards was a common illness during the period is suggested by the unusually accurate detail given in its description. The motions were always to be observed to see if their appearance 'is thin, some is suffused with thick humours, some mingled with fragments of the inwards and of the small guts, some is very

bloody, some comes from the bowels ... the man feels sore at
his navel and very sore on his shoulders, and thirst and loss
of appetite is present and a little blood drops through the
back passage'.[86] On the other hand, constipation was not
overlooked and various remedies suggested include the
drinking of wormwood and butter in sour ale.[87] For painful
bowel evacuation, waybroad (plantain), elder rind and
salt, all dissolved in ale, are prescribed.[88] Ordinary diarrhoea was treated by eating honey and wheaten meal boiled
with unsalted fat and wax.[89]

Poor, inadequate diet combined with exposure to the
weather must have caused various circulatory disorders and
chilblains, at least, were suffered by large sections of the
population. Meadow-wort, lustmock and oak rind mixed
with honey were to be taken; alternatively, if the hands were
affected, they were to be wrapped in linen after having been
rubbed with sulphur, white frankincense and oil.[90]

A further group of disorders which troubled both Anglo-
Saxon and Anglo-Norman communities were mental illnesses, and attempts to alleviate them are relatively common
in the texts. For 'mental vacancy and against folly, put into
ale bishopwort, lupins, betony, fennel, water agrimony,
cockle etc. and let him drink'. 'For idiocy and folly, put into
ale, cassia and lupins, bishopwort, alexanders, githrife
[corn cockle], field more and holy water, let him drink.'[91]
To cure a 'wit sick man' a concoction containing bishopwort, lupin, strawberry plant, pennyroyal and others was
boiled in butter and strained; then nine masses were said and
the mixture was put in a bucket of cold water. The sick man
was bathed in this water and given blessed bread, cheese and
garlic to eat. After some herbal ointment had been applied
to his body, a purgative medicine was given.[92] Various
herbal remedies are also suggested for mental instability and,
in particular, mandrake, St John's wort and periwinkle
were regarded as especially effective.

In the earlier non-medical literature, the management of
the lunatic or the mentally disturbed was often to bind their

limbs until the acute phase had subsided. It was unfortunate when an epileptic was so treated, but several instances occur which suggest that this did happen. Holy water was frequently given in the hope of exorcising evil spirits, and various relics, charms and prayers were employed for the same purpose.

The notion of exorcising evil spirits was probably behind this use of binding and violence towards the patient. Indeed, one recommendation advises that, 'in case a man be a lunatic, take the skin of a mereswine [porpoise], make it into a whip and strike the man with it, soon he will be well'.[93]

Bede writes of various attempts to cure insanity and those not involving the use of religious rites or relics usually consisted of crude forms of restraint. A guest at Bardney Abbey who was frequently 'troubled in the night by an unclean spirit . . . was suddenly possessed by the devil and began to gnash his teeth and foam at the mouth . . . he could neither be held down nor bound . . .'[94] What this illness was is not certain, though it was more likely to be an epileptic attack than insanity, but recourse to confinement was obviously considered the normal procedure.

Later, in Norman England, similar treatment was recommended. When Ailred of Rievaulx was once attacked by a mad monk, he refused to have the sick man 'beaten or bound or fettered as a madman'.[95]

The remedial value of dieting was well recognised and the leech was able to advise on many foods which were either to be taken or refused. The Anglo-Saxon physician regarded hens, geese, pigs' feet and the meat of the kid and boar as easily digestible; while rabbit, goat, duck and venison were considered rather more difficult to digest. In cases of jaundice, after the blood-letting 'the man's diet is to be considered'. Soups, eggs and meat have to be avoided, as well as all greasy foods. Abstention from wine was also advised, while well-moistened bread and a mixture of vinegar and honey was prescribed as especially beneficial.[96]

Pregnant women were to avoid the meat of the bull, buck, cock, ram, boar or goose. It was thought that if such male flesh was eaten, there was the distinct possibility of giving birth to a deformed child.[97]

Bald's second leechbook contains many examples of suggested diets for various internal disorders, especially those of the stomach; and advice contained in the *Peri-Didaxeon* states that various kinds of meat should be avoided, particularly that of cattle, while recommending dry bread and cheese for several disorders of the chest including asthma. However, for this same illness, chicken and worm-wood, laurel berries and oil of roses made into an ointment for the chest are prescribed and a drink made from soaking chicken in wine and oil is to be given.[98]

From the texts available it is clear that physicians paid considerable attention to diets, and eating and drinking in excess were generally regarded as unwise.

The leeches, in their day-to-day practice, have now been seen attempting to grapple with the diseases and ailments of their time. Selective and fragmentary as this account must be, some indication has been given of the methods used by the Old English physician, who, while strictly limited by the availability of supplies and his reliance upon botanical medicines, did offer more sophisticated treatment on occasion. He prepared and used vapour baths, salves and ointments, plaster, potions and powders. He considered that he had a remedy for the most varied of complaints and always seemed supremely confident in the effectiveness of his prescriptions. The chances of any relief, beyond the most transient, in most cases must have been remote, however, and if, by the very nature of many of the minor ailments, spontaneous improvement occurred, then the leech would enjoy his enhanced reputation. The general population may well have adopted a more philosophical, not to say stoical attitude to disease than is now the custom; but none the less, the Anglo-Saxon leech did try to alleviate the sickness and distress from which his patients suffered and carried out his work with at least some regard to the ethics and morality of his calling.

5
Surgery

There can be little doubt that in Anglo-Saxon England, and later into Norman times, surgical procedures were frequently resorted to, though equally certain is the fact that precious little definite evidence has survived to indicate how such operations were performed or for what conditions they were recommended.

The medical sources, as already briefly noted, contain some references to what are obviously surgical practices and, in addition, further evidence is found in the non-medical literature of the period. These references are tantalisingly few in number and in detail.

As far as the practitioner who performed the operations is concerned, it is not clear whether there was a professional surgeon distinct in function from the physician or whether the latter, if called upon, would perform whatever surgery lay within his competence. There are, however, certain references to the surgeon as such, so it may just be possible that some separation of functions could have taken place in the later years of the Anglo-Saxon period and more probably in post-Conquest times. In the earlier times it is almost certain that the two terms physician or leech and surgeon were interchangeable. For example, Cynefrith, who performed an operation on St Aethelthryth, Abbess of Ely, was, according to Bede, a *medicus* or physician. He carried out an operation to drain a large tubercular swelling under the abbess's jaw, clearly a surgical procedure.[1]

Having regard to the type of society existing at the time, which must have been relatively violent, to the very great risk of accident from the farming of hard, unbroken ground and, in general, as a consequence of a difficult and rigorous life, it is probable that the most common surgical conditions from which the Saxon population suffered would be those concerned with fractured bones, dislocated joints and wounds of all kinds. This is confirmed to some extent by the fact that of all the literary references to surgery which are available, the majority involve these types of traumatic conditions. In corroboration, archaeological evidence shows that Pott's fracture of the ankle, for instance, was one of the most common fracture injuries sustained, as one would expect in communities living in primitive farming conditions where there was continuous expansion into woodland which would require clearance of very difficult ground (see chapter 1).

As early as the eighth century, Bede cites several examples of people sustaining fractures and indicates the treatment given. He tells the story of Herebald, who was riding in the company of John of Beverley when he fell off his horse and, in addition to internal injuries, suffered fractures of his skull and thumb. Bishop John thereupon called for the services of a doctor who bound up the injured man's skull. His treatment was successful enough to enable Herebald to continue his journey soon afterwards.[2]

A second early example of treatment for a fracture is contained in the *Life of Wilfrid*. In this case a young mason named Bothelm is said to have fallen from the top of Hexham church, breaking various bones and dislocating some joints. Physicians were called in to immobilise the fractured limbs with bandages.[3]

That splinting was a common treatment for fractures can be determined from the leechbooks, where fractures and dislocations are discussed and their treatment by immobilisation is suggested. Indeed, the Old English word for a splint (*spelc*) is frequently mentioned in these medical texts. It is, for instance, the recommended treatment for a broken leg after the limb has been bathed in a hot herbal bath. Incidentally this paragraph recognises the fact that when the thigh is fractured, the muscles frequently go into strong spasm which involves the danger of the fractured bone ends overriding with consequent leg shortening. The leechbook has this to say:

> In the case of many a man where his feet shrink up to his thighs [ie limb shortening due to muscle spasm] give baths . . . when they [the limbs] are in a sweat, then let the patient arrange the bones as well as he can and apply a splint . . .[4]

It is curious that in this case the splinting is to be done by the patient himself, but it is clear that the importance of immobilisation is accepted which could well enable some form of traction or reduction to be attempted subsequently.

Splinting alone is never suggested; it is merely carried out in conjunction with various herbal remedies. Another prescription given for a fractured leg is one in which a salve or ointment is to be prepared from bonewort (pansy or violet?) mixed with egg white and applied to the limb, but before the splint is used a layer of elm bark is to be laid on to the part, apparently as a substitute for a dressing.[5]

Another interesting treatment for a fracture, in this case of the skull, is described in Bald's first leechbook. After recommending a complicated herbal mixture, the prescription continues, 'if the brain be exposed, take the yolk of an egg and mix a little with honey and fill the wound and bind it up with tow [flax or hemp] and so let it alone . . .'.[6] This compound could act as an adhesive to assist in containing the brain tissue. In contrast to this is the treatment for the same kind of fracture contained in the *Anglo-Saxon Herbal*. This suggests that the herb betony be rubbed to powder and two drams of it taken in hot beer. In spite of its obvious futility, the remedy is considered so successful that the prescription concludes with the words '. . . the head heals very quickly after the drink'.[7]

Before leaving fractures of the skull, one further interesting item is included in the third leechbook. It must refer to a depressed fracture, for the paragraph reads, 'If there be a broken bone in the head and it will not come away, pound green betony and lay it on the wound frequently till the bones come away and the wound is mended.'[8] Many other remedies for fractured bones are contained in the various texts but all are of a similar nature to the examples noted above.

A good example of the treatment advocated for dislocated joints occurs in the same paragraph as that concerning the depressed fracture of the skull. For a dislocated shoulder it is suggested that a salve containing a number of herbs mixed with butter be applied when warm to the joint, and this is all that is required, apparently, for the successful reduction of the dislocation. No evidence in the leechbooks or elsewhere suggests that dislocations could be reduced by traction or other mechanical methods, although these cannot be absolutely ruled out in view of the small amount of medical literature surviving. It would seem, therefore, that except for cases of spontaneous reduction, there was little hope of a successful outcome, and consequently deformity and loss of function could be expected.

It will come as no surprise that the leechbooks contain many remedies for wounds, both internal and external. In the first and third leechbooks, for instance, there are prescriptions using groups of drinks and salves which contain a variety of herbs, butter, honey and eggs.[9] The antiseptic properties of honey were recognised, for many recipes are suggested containing honey to clean wounds. A typical example recommends, '. . . take clean honey, warm it at the fire and put it in a clean vessel, add salt and stir the mixture until it becomes thick, then smear the wound with this when it becomes foul'.[10] Another prescription for the prevention of sepsis is to apply a mixture made up of briar and other plants.

An internal wound could be treated with a drink consisting of wine, oil, comfrey and honey, or there is a remedy containing herbs boiled in ale and fermented yeast which was to be taken by mouth.

A noteworthy aspect of wound management is indicated in another sub-section of the first leechbook. Following a recipe for a wound ointment, it continues '. . . if the edges of the wound are too high, run them round with a hot iron very lightly, so that the skin may whiten'.[11] This is quite a rational piece of advice for wounds which were over-granulating and so would heal superficially while the underlying structures might remain infected. Cauterisation is here suggested to prevent this.

Burns are also given consideration and several recipes are given for their treatment in the *Leechbook of Bald*, the *Anglo-Saxon Herbal* and the *Medicina de Quadrupedibus*.[12] A rather uncongenial prescription uses a mixture of goat's droppings and wheat burnt to dust and then added to butter and boiled. After this concoction has been strained, it is to be applied to the burnt area.[13]

Perhaps more useful treatments are those in which the plant fennel mixed with old grease is to be applied to the part, or lily and yarrow boiled in butter and laid on to the burn.[14] A further remedy recommends simply the frequent application of the white of an egg. The use of butter, egg and grease (fat) would certainly have a soothing effect upon the burn and is a further example of the empirical nature of much of the treatment prescribed in this period. Moreover, there is a remarkable differentiation made between burns caused by hot solids and those by hot liquids:

. . . if a man is burnt with fire only, take woodruff and lily, and brooklime; boil in butter and smear this on. If a man be burnt with a liquid, let him take elm rind [inner layer of bark] and roots of lily, boil them in milk and smear on three times a day. For sunburn, boil in butter tender ivy twigs and smear this on.[15]

This, incidentally, is one of the rare occasions where daily frequency of treatment is prescribed.

As far as actual surgical techniques are concerned, there are some references in the *Leechbook of Bald*, but just how much is a description of the writer's own practice, and how much mere copying from earlier (perhaps foreign) sources, is now hard to determine. It does not seem very likely that Anglo-Saxon surgeons did in fact perform these operations, in view of the general standards of the time, but attempts at surgical intervention cannot be completely ruled out. One of the most detailed descriptions of an operation contained in any of the texts is of the procedure considered necessary to cure 'hardness of the liver' or liver abscess.[16] However, C. H. Talbot has shown that this section stems from the works of Gariopontus and Petrocellus, both of which derive from a ninth-century continental source.[17]

Firstly it is advised that the painful swelling should be bathed in hot water containing various herbs, and that this bathing should be continued for three days. After this time a further mixture containing honey, groats, wine, laurel berries and other plants is to be drunk for another three days. For a further three days, a cupping glass or horn is to be used to 'draw out' any excess secretions. Diuretic drinks are prescribed and further herbal medicines given when it becomes clear that the abscess has burst, and then it is advised that all means are to be used to encourage the passing of water in order to assist the removal of the escaping pus. How pus from the liver could be passed in the urine is not explained. The knowledge shown in the following section is accurate enough, however, to suggest personal experience of this disorder, for the actual instructions are as follows:

> When the swelling has become an abscess and bursts and it becomes more pain free and [the pus] is passing off downwards through the body and the man passes pus [in the urine] it is possible that he will be cured; then he must be given principally diuretic drinks in order that all the mischief through the body may be cleansed, for fear that the man should begin to vomit.

Even more surprising is the following paragraph which deals
with the case in the event of the abscess growing but not
spontaneously bursting, and therefore requiring surgical
attention. The writer continues: 'If, however, the swelling
and the pus increase to that degree that it seems that it must
be cut into to let it out . . .' it is necessary to bathe the place
with herbal fomentations similar to those used in the first
three days of treatment. Following this preliminary treatment, a not very deep incision is made, but care must be
taken that the contents of the abscess are not allowed to
escape. The loss of blood is to be kept to a minimum 'lest the
sick man become too languid or die' and then the wound
should be slowly enlarged and through the opening a syringe
or tube is inserted in order to wash out the cavity. Should
the wound become septic, however, honey is recommended
to clean the area. Finally, if the hardening of the liver has
become chronic and the swelling cannot be cured (cirrhosis
of the liver and/or ascites?), then the same herbal fomentations are to be used, and blood-letting from the right arm is
suggested.

This section has been dealt with at some length in order to
illustrate that among so much worthless material, there is
occasionally the glimmering of rational treatment, even if
the original ideas and practices may in fact have been taken
from the Classical world.

A further example of Anglo-Saxon surgery, in which some
knowledge of good technique and observation is displayed,
occurs in the section concerning amputations. The operation
is usually performed to prevent the spread of gangrene, a
condition likely to have been prevalent because of the poor
hygienic standards of the time. All wounds and open injuries
would be at great risk and, in spite of the frequent use of
honey as an antiseptic recommended throughout the leechbooks, it must be certain that gangrene was an ever-present
threat.

In the first leechbook the following surgical instructions
are given:

If the discoloured body be in such a bad condition that there is no feeling in it, then you must cut off all the dead and the unfeeling flesh as far as the living part so that there will be no dead flesh remaining. After that the wound shall be healed as you would the part which still has feeling.

The after-care varies with the age of the patient, whether man, woman or child, whether busy or idle, whether strong or weak. The actual technique for the amputation is remarkably accurate.

If you must cut off an unhealthy limb from a healthy body, then do not cut to the limit of the healthy flesh, but cut further into the whole and quick flesh, so that a better and quicker cure may be obtained. When you set fire on the man [ie cauterise], take leaves of tender leek and grated salt, overlay the places so that the heat of the fire be more quickly drawn away.[18]

Here is a fine description of gangrene with sensible clinical instructions to ensure the removal of some healthy tissues beyond the limit of the gangrenous area so as to assist in the sound healing of the wound. Finally, the concluding piece of advice is to apply honey to help in the removal of the subsequent scab formation.

If these internal operations and amputations were, in fact, performed, it is worth inquiring if any anaesthetic or other means of pain relief was employed.

As far as English sources are concerned, nowhere is precise information given as to the nature of any sleep-inducing or pain-relieving drugs used in surgical procedures. There are, however, a few plants recommended in the herbals which are recognised as possessing narcotic properties; whether they were specifically administered for the purpose of surgery is not known.

Mandrake, for example, must have been regarded as useful for, in the *Anglo-Saxon Herbal*, it is prescribed for those who cannot sleep;[19] similarly in this text poppy is recommended for sleeplessness, it 'sendest sleep on him'.[20] The first leechbook mentions a rub with poppy and oil as useful for 'much wakefulness'.[21]

Also in the *Anglo-Saxon Herbal*, iris is thought to possess the virtue of 'sleep bearing',[22] while henbane is also considered to have narcotic properties. Whether these and the other plants were thought useful merely to procure sleep, or were regarded as anaesthetics to render the patient quiet during his operation, it is not now possible to ascertain.

In the twelfth-century *Life of St Kentigern*, there is a slight indication that anaesthesia was known and used in surgery. The author, Joceline, tells of a preparation called *letargion* being used on people who 'suffered incision and sometimes burning of the limbs (cautery) and the abrasion even of the vitals, and after awakening from the sleep have been ignorant of what was done to them'.[23] Moreover, a little later in the mid-thirteenth century, Bartolomeus Anglicus thought that mandrake, when given in wine, would deaden sensation in a man undergoing surgery. It is unfortunate that these odd brief references are all that can be put forward in favour of the use of anaesthesia during this period, but to suggest anything more definite would be to overstrain the available evidence.

The suturing of wounds and operation incisions was not, apparently, beyond the competence of the Saxon leech. A plastic-surgical operation for the repair of hare-lip is described in which the use of silk sutures is required.[24] In this operation there is recognition of the risk that sometimes the tissues can contract, producing deformity, for there is the instruction that, should this occur, the surgeon must smooth out the tightened tissues by hand.

Another instance of suturing after an operation is contained in a description of the operation required to reduce a prolapsed bowel and, in this case again, silk sutures are recommended.[25] It is suggested that the prolapsed bowel be 'put back into the man and sew up with silk . . .'. No doubt the silk used for the manufacture of sutures was obtained from abroad, as this is another commodity mentioned as

I

being imported by the merchant in Aelfric's *Colloquy*. Although silk was the material used for sutures in the *Leechbook of Bald* and elsewhere, this was certainly not the only material employed in the attempt to ensure successful healing.[26]

Other surgical procedures undertaken were those for the removal of cataracts and polypi, and there is a twelfth-century illustration which shows these two operations in progress.[27] Unfortunately, this carries no text other than the words, 'Cataracts of the eyes are thus cut out.' This part of the drawing shows the surgeon making an incision into the right eye of a patient. The second part shows the surgeon holding a knife which is inserted into the patient's nose, while in his other hand he holds a tube which appears to be keeping the nostril open. The patient is holding a bowl to collect the blood which is draining from his nose. The brief description of this picture runs: 'Polyps are thus cut from the nose.'

An earlier illustration, this time from the eleventh century, shows the operation for gout, cautery points around the knee joint 'for tumour and pain of the knees' and also those for hernia situated in the groin. In addition, the operation for haemorrhoids is illustrated. This last procedure is of interest in that the surgeon is shown holding a large knife cutting into the haemorrhoids while, at the same time, holding open the buttocks with a retractor.[28]

A technique used to introduce fluids into the body is suggested by the treatment recommended for 'wind and nausea'. This leechdom prescribes the herbs rue and laurel added to ale, together with oil-soaked fennel seed; this mixture to be 'introduced through a pipe or a horn as leeches know how'.[29] Possibly this refers to treatment by clysters or enemas. Similar treatment is prescribed in other parts of the second leechbook for both constipation and retention of urine.[30]

Cupping was another procedure used by the Anglo-Saxons. This involved the use of a glass or horn cup which was alternately applied and released over the affected part; its effect was to suck up the tissues, acting as a form of massage and also as a means of dispersing and drawing out secretions and blood. Cupping would also be used after blood-letting and scarification to facilitate the blood flow.[31]

Scarification was frequently employed, and involved superficial scratching or cutting of the skin, sometimes being self-inflicted. It is likely that it produced a counter-irritant effect, so assisting in the removal of more deep-seated discomfort. Ointments were sometimes applied to the scarified area, as is advised in the case of pleurisy.[32] In other cases, scarification was to be frequently repeated, for example, to areas of paralysis.[33] It was also performed as a mild alternative to blood-letting. There is a prescription for healing the scarification cuts. Bean, oat or barley meal was to be mixed with vinegar and honey and the resulting paste applied to the cut area.[34] On the other hand, in the *Peri-Didaxeon* occurs the instruction to rub salt into the wounds of the scarified area, no doubt to enhance the irritant effect.[35]

A more severe procedure frequently adopted was that of cauterisation. It was used not only in the treatment of various diseases where it could conceivably be of some help, but also in cases where it would be quite useless. Cauterisation, like many other remedies used by the Anglo-Saxons, had been practised long before their time and much of its appeal was due to superstitious influences. Where wounds were granulating excessively, cautery may have been a rational choice,[36] but several illustrations show how useless much of it must have been. One from the eleventh century shows a human body with the various cautery points indicated, and other eleventh- to thirteenth-century illustrations show cautery in actual progress for various disorders.[37] It is probable that these illustrations are copies of earlier Classical work but, nevertheless, they indicate the sort of treatment the leech would endeavour to carry out.

During the twelfth century and after, the use of cautery became more commonplace as the influence of Arabic medicine became more widely felt in England. It was highly thought of by the Moslem physicians who regarded it as an effective means of eliminating 'corrupt matter', preventing haemorrhage or limiting the spread of infection.

From English illustrations it would seem that cautery was applied by hot irons to certain fixed points, these depending upon the illness concerned. These charts, mostly of twelfth-century date, were apparently intended to ensure accuracy of application and the cautery irons themselves appear to be thin pointed instruments rather like very large needles or rods.

A more complicated form of cauterisation is shown in an eleventh-century illustration at the front of one of the existing copies of the *Anglo-Saxon Herbal*. There are four pictures contained within this illustration, one of which represents a patient suffering from gout who, in addition to having his feet cut, is having some corrosive fluid applied to them by his physician.[38] The fluid would burn the tissues in a similar fashion to the cautery iron. The caption to the picture runs: '. . . a podagric [sufferer from gout] is cut and burned thus.'

BLOOD-LETTING

Blood-letting, venesection or *minutio* was a surgical procedure frequently employed throughout the whole period covered by this book. It has already been noted in chapter 2 that as early as John of Beverley's time in the seventh century, not only was blood-letting performed, but it had already acquired complicated formulae as to the most propitious times for its success.

In the monasteries, venesection was commonly practised and various relaxations of the monastic rule were granted to those being bled. It was, for instance, one of the few occasions when a monk was permitted to vary his frugal diet with more nourishing fare; he was allowed periods for talking in the guests' parlour, particularly after dinner and in the evening when the rest of the brethren were at prayers and, not least, he was granted the comfort of a fire. Indeed, one record (*c* 1280) observed that for the three days during which the bleeding continues, the monks under treatment are to be provided with 'a clean napkin and towels, goblets and spoons, and all utensils that they will require, and he (the monk in charge or the Infirmarian) ought to bestow upon them all the comfort and kindness in his power, for those who have been bled ought during that period to lead a life of joy and freedom from care in comfort and happiness'.[39] Very often a special room was provided for venesection in the monastic infirmary, but if this was not possible, the general amenities of the infirmary were placed at the patient's disposal.

At an earlier date than this, evidence exists that bleeding was one of the very few times when any form of comfort was permitted to members of the monastic community. For instance, Abbot Warin of St Albans (1183–95), himself a physician, allowed absence from night prayers, arranged for those being bled to have earlier meals and, in general, made life a little more tolerable. It would seem that as time went by, what had originally been considered a purely remedial measure was now also an occasion for having a day's rest, for Abbot Warin ruled that if the permitted second day's relaxation was interrupted by the occurrence of a feast day, it should be made up on the following day.[40]

From the earliest times, one of the principal reasons for *minutio* was the belief that too much blood in the body was the cause of disease. It was thought that particular veins should be opened to cure particular illnesses. Blood-letting was performed according to a fixed anatomical system which had little regard for the patient's condition. For example, an entry in Bald's first leechbook which concerns the treatment for 'dry' disease, thought to be a wasting disorder – possibly consumption – prescribes that blood-letting be performed on the vein 'below the ankle'.[41] Again, in the second leechbook, where blood-letting is only a part of the sick man's treatment, it is recommended 'in early spring from the left arm'.[42]

The times, days or seasons during which bleeding was to be undertaken were considered of paramount importance, and the most complicated astrological, lunar and calendar

details are written into the texts to provide the reader with
the greatest possible chance of success. For example, Bald's
first leechbook says '. . . and there is no time for bloodletting
so good as in early Lent, when the evil humours are gathered
. . . and on the Kalends of April best of all, when trees and
plants first sprout . . .'.[43] Perhaps this reflects the view that
bleeding could return to normal the various altered
'humours' which were regarded as the cause of disease.
Venesection should not be performed on holy days, the
Egyptian Days and the various Mondays, all of which have
already been referred to in chapter 2. The first leechbook, in
the section just quoted, has an item headed 'On what season
bloodletting is not to be performed and on what it is best to
be practised', followed by various seasonal formulae. The
rules in their earliest form go back to the time of Hippocrates.

This chapter from the leechbook also contains various
recommendations for the treatment of haemorrhage and
sepsis, two risks which must always have attended such practices. We are told that 'if a lancet wound grows corrupt, take
mallow leaves, boil in water and bathe the wound, also lay
on to the wound the root of the mallow. If you want to stop
blood running from the incision, take kettle soot, rub it to
dust and sprinkle it on the wound.' Further: 'If you cannot
stop a gushing vein, take some of the escaping blood, dry it
on a hot stone and rub it to dust, lay the dust on the vein and
tie up strongly.' This treatment suggests a pressure bandage
or tourniquet. A significant part of this chapter deals with the
serious consequences that could follow venesection: 'If in
bloodletting a man is cut upon a sinew, mingle together wax
and pitch and sheep's fat, lay on a cloth and on to the
cut.'

That there was some regularity in the practice of blood-
letting is shown from monastic routines. It would seem that
a seven-week cycle was in operation, at least in some religious
orders, for example the Augustinians at Barnwell, Cambridgeshire, for arrangements were included in their rule for

those who found it necessary to let blood more frequently. Indeed, so seriously did they view venesection that on the second day of their rest, the brethren were even excused attendance at mass for fear that they might hurt the arm from which the blood had been taken.[44] Moreover, the importance attached to bleeding can be indicated by the fact that this was the only remedial procedure or treatment, together with that of cautery, which was permitted to the monks of the very strict Carthusian order.

There can be no doubt that many monks sought venesection as a means of acquiring a rest, opportunities for talk and gossip, better food and even a holiday.[45] The monks' practice of venesection persisted throughout the whole of the Middle Ages and is known to have been performed regularly well into modern times.

In view of the complicated lunar formulae and superstitious rites which had attached themselves to blood-letting, the practice of venesection involved curious conventions at home and abroad. Walter Map, the courtier of Henry II, tells the story that when Count Theobald IV of Blois (1102–52) was being besieged and surrounded by Louis VII of France, it so happened that Theobald had been bled two days earlier. Because of this, Louis lifted the siege, saying, 'I wished to prevent an excellent man hearing by my means of anything sinister at the time of his blood-letting which might occasion his death.'[46]

Another example, also from abroad, of the irrational views sometimes taken regarding the letting of blood is one in which a resulting catastrophe seems to be calmly accepted. An educated clerk, after having been bled, suffered a loss of his knowledge of letters and learning 'as if it had passed out of him with his blood' so that he remembered no Latin for a full year. At a subsequent bleeding a year later, however, he recovered his faculties.[47]

Various mishaps must have occurred during blood-letting. We have seen already that Bede describes what is almost certainly a case of sepsis or haematoma in a nun's arm.[48]

Later, remedies are contained in the leechbooks for cut tendons, and later still are the descriptions of precautions taken in the monasteries after the venesection.

The operation itself was performed with a lancet or surgeon's knife and the Anglo-Saxon vocabulary for some of the surgical instruments has survived. The Old English words *snidisen, aedre-seax* (vein knife) or *blodseax* all denote a lancet or scalpel; the surgeon's knife was a *laece-seax* (leech's knife) and the word *laecegetawu* referred to medical and surgical instruments generally; *laeceiron* distinguished those instruments made of iron; a medical chest to contain these instruments was called a *laececist*.[49]

LEGAL ATTITUDE TO PERSONAL INJURY

Various legal codes surviving from the Anglo-Saxon period lay down the compensation or *bot* payable in money or in kind by an assailant in respect of any personal injury inflicted upon his victim. These show an almost complete lack of knowledge of anatomical and physiological function.

Many fundamental anomalies occur in these laws concerning the relationship between a particular injury and its monetary value payable as compensation. An insight into which parts of the body were regarded as important by the Saxons can be gained by a comparison of certain injuries or mutilations with the amount of compensation demanded.[50]

Compensation was introduced gradually in order to provide some acceptable alternative to the traditional pagan Saxon 'blood feud', and as the Christian Church spread its influence, this more peaceful method of settling disputes became established. There are two main tariffs or lists of compensation payments in the Anglo-Saxon laws, one dating from as early as King Ethelbert of Kent in the seventh century and the other from the reign of King Alfred the Great in the ninth century.

It should perhaps be noted that even if the injuries sustained were the result of accident or self-defence, compensation had still to be paid; innocence of intention did not remove liability.[51]

Before any detailed consideration is given to the actual payments, it is necessary to digress a little to discuss the position of the Anglo-Saxon in his society; we must assess just how the monetary and other payments for personal injury compared with those imposed for different offences against the law.

In Anglo-Saxon law, every person had a *wergild* or 'man-price' which was payable to the next of kin on an individual's death from other than natural causes. The amount of this *wergild* depended upon the social rank of the deceased. Of course, the amounts awarded in Ethelbert's tariff cannot easily be compared with those awarded for similar injuries in Alfred's code; it is difficult to establish an economic relationship between the two currencies, separated as they are by two centuries.

Compensation payments were awarded for many different offences in addition to homicide, and most of them were also related to the social status of the victim. There was therefore a sliding scale of payments, varying with the position in society of the injured party, rather than the severity of the offence. Thus, the compensation payable for an offence against a *thegn* or noble was rated higher than that for a similar offence against a *ceorl* or ordinary freeman.

It has been generally accepted that compensation for personal injury also employed this sliding scale of payments. But this is not borne out by study of the tariffs themselves. In the case of physical damage to the individual, it was the injury alone which was the criterion, and the victim's place in society was largely irrelevant so long as he did not die. The only exception to this rule applied to the clergy; one of King Cnut's laws stipulated that compensation for injury to a member of the clergy should vary according to his clerical rank.[52] It is possible that this was a special concession granted to the Church, but even here it was the clerical rank of the victim which determined the compensation value, not the social class to which the priest had formerly belonged.

Ethelbert's tariff contains fifty-six different types of injury, and Alfred's list has fifty-nine varied injuries. It is reasonable to assume that these refer to the more common wounds, mutilations and disabilities from which the general population suffered. They show that Anglo-Saxon society was somewhat uninhibited in the use of violence towards the person, and both sword and spear wounds are much in evidence.

A brief survey of both tariffs will show anomalies which suggest strongly that there was little recognition of the seriousness of one injury as against another. Occasionally, however, there is indication of an awareness that a particular injury might deserve higher compensation than one of a similar kind with less extensive damage.

These laws are very detailed, with particular emphasis being given to injuries of the hands, fingers, feet and toes, these being the parts of the body most affected by sword and spear fighting and also of particular value to the average individual for his agricultural livelihood. This emphasis apart, the compensations awarded for most of these injuries are illogical. Ethelbert's code, for example (clause 54), awards 20 shillings if a thumb is cut off; the loss of an index finger is valued at only 9 shillings (clause 54.2) but 11 shillings is the value awarded for the loss of the little finger (clause 54.5).[53] What justification those drafting these laws could see in awarding more for the loss of a little finger than the very important index finger is not entirely clear, even when its action in gripping a sword or farming implement is taken into account. Similarly obscure is the fact the fifth finger is valued at over half the sum awarded for the loss of the thumb without which a hand is virtually useless.

Alfred's tariff shows a similar absence of any real functional knowledge. For the loss of a thumb, 30 shillings is to be paid; 15 shillings for an index finger; 17 shillings for the ring finger; 12 shillings for the middle finger and 9 shillings for the little finger (clauses 55–60). Here again the index finger appears undervalued; there can be no functional reason for this as the ring finger is in no way vital to the adequate function of the hand. However, the ring finger was considered the 'medical' or 'leech' finger and could therefore possibly have had some importance in a medico-magical context. More significant, perhaps, rings were very popular and were given as rewards for bravery and loyal service so there could well have been in addition to these foregoing reasons some aesthetic or cosmetic purpose for overvaluing this finger; in both tariffs considerable concern for the personal appearance of the individual can frequently be seen. Indeed, if one feature above all others is demonstrated in these laws, it is precisely this concern for personal appearance.

Similar anomalies abound throughout the tariffs, the compensation for loss of teeth is a good example, which also illustrates the Anglo-Saxon's preoccupation with personal appearance. Ethelbert's code (clause 61) provides as follows: for the loss of each of the four front teeth (incisors), 6 shillings must be paid, for each canine tooth lost, 3 shillings is required, while 1 shilling is awarded for the loss of any tooth beyond the canines, ie the molars. Here the emphasis is again on appearance rather than function. The canine teeth seem highly valued; this is even more apparent in Alfred's code (clause 49) where the loss of a canine is compensated by the sum of 15 shillings compared with only 8 shillings for a front tooth and 4 shillings for molars. The reason for this is hard to determine, unless it is that human canines were regarded as good luck charms in the same way that animal canine teeth were used for amulets.

As mentioned earlier, among the large group of anomalous legal clauses, there are a few which, either by accident or from medical knowledge, show a more rational recognition of degrees of disability. In Alfred's code (clause 66), if a hand is lost, the compensation is 66 shillings, $3\frac{1}{3}$ pence, but if the forearm is also involved, the compensation is raised to 80 shillings. Again, in Alfred's tariff (clause 70), for a simple fracture of a rib, 10 shillings is payable but if it be a compound fracture, the award is increased to 15 shillings. Further, clause 75 lays down that if a tendon is injured but is expected to recover, then 12 shillings is to be awarded but if a recovery is impossible and lameness or a limp results, the compensation is raised to 30 shillings. Needless to say, any degree of lameness, however slight, would be a serious handicap for a Saxon farmer and would therefore require exceptional recompense.

From the study of these two sets of laws, two principal facts emerge, both of which give a valuable insight into Anglo-Saxon society: firstly that a society as early as that of the seventh to tenth centuries which could conceive and produce such detailed tariffs for the protection of its citizens surely reflects a rare political stability; secondly, and perhaps more important for our purpose, they show that the Anglo-Saxon took a great interest in his appearance. Any injury, however slight, which could detract from his good looks was sure to be awarded a compensation in excess of its intrinsic severity. A glance at the clauses in both codes dealing with injuries to the face and head shows this concern clearly.

That the Saxon had a love of ornate, colourful and luxurious dress is well documented; examples exist from all periods of criticism being levelled at this addiction. Here, in these laws, is independent confirmation of the Anglo-Saxon's vanity. Such leading figures as Aldhelm and Alcuin and later commentators such as William of Malmesbury all had harsh words to say on the Anglo-Saxon love of extravagant adornment and appearance. Alcuin, for example, in a letter to King Ethelred of Northumbria in AD 793, calls attention to the way people were dressing in luxurious clothes and trimming their hair 'to resemble the pagans' and in a letter to Higbald, Bishop of Lindisfarne, and his monks, also dated 793, he implores them not to 'glory in the vanity of raiment...'. Later, in the early years of the twelfth century, the English were described as having 'their beards shaven, their arms laden with golden bracelets; their skin adorned with punctured designs'[54] referring to their contemporary habits.

The value and beauty of some of the jewellery and clothing is evidenced in contemporary wills. Items such as fur gowns, cloaks and robes, gold hairbands and other personal ornaments all appear.

To summarise, the laws show a lack of appreciation of the functional results of injuries, which points to a corresponding deficiency in the knowledge of surgical theory and practice. It seems evident that the higher ranks of society, for whom these laws were chiefly though not entirely composed, were more concerned with honour and appearance than with the more practical and mundane issues of physical disability.

6

The Problem of Leprosy

To the medieval mind, leprosy was a collective term under which many conditions and eruptions of the skin were included, and it is necessary to look at this disease through the eyes of both the sufferer and the general population during those centuries when its incidence caused a considerable social problem.

Conditions of the skin such as psoriasis, eczema, erisypelas, scrofula, lupus and many forms of ulcer and scab which could produce an external suppuration of pus were frequently diagnosed as leprosy; it is thought that even syphilis[1] was included under the general term. A patient would, therefore, show a scaly skin disorder or severe rash at his peril.

This confusion arose due to the form of the Greek word *lepra* which in the succeeding centuries became loosely used to describe not only the true disease, or Hansen's Disease, as it is now called, but many others which came to be regarded as leprosy. The word *lepra* meaning scaly was, as far as the Greeks were concerned, used not in relation to leprosy as we know it today, but to refer to the many scaling skin diseases such as eczema and psoriasis. Their word to describe true leprosy was *elephantiasis*, which emphasised one of the more obvious and recognisable symptoms of the disorder, that of the thickening and coarseness of the skin. *Elephantiasis graecorum* became confused in the course of time with *lepra graecorum* which, as has been already seen, described a very different group of skin diseases which were not necessarily infectious or contagious. Gradually, however, *lepra* became the term in common currency for leprosy, no doubt due to contemporary convenience.

There is little evidence of true leprosy before the first century AD in the Western world and it is likely that the disease spread from Asia as there are records which suggest that it was present in China before its appearance in the West.

In England, the earliest cases of true leprosy so far discovered date from about the seventh century; they are found in skeletons from the Island of Tean, Isles of Scilly, and from Burwell, Cambridgeshire.[2] From then on the disease appears to have increased slowly in frequency until it reached its maximum degree of prevalence during the period from the eleventh to thirteenth centuries, after which its incidence gradually began to decline. It is desirable to keep a sense of proportion as to its degree of prevalence as it was by no means the widespread and intensely contagious condition that the medieval chroniclers would have us believe. There is no doubt that the number of cases was sufficient to ensure that it was a substantial social and medical problem, but more often than not its incidence was confined to a few cases here and there in the countryside, with perhaps a somewhat more frequent occurrence in the towns.

Leprosy was no respecter of persons and both high and low in society were affected by it. Aelfweard, Bishop of London, for example, who was also Abbot of Evesham, was forced to retire to his monastery at Evesham because of his leprosy. The monks there would not permit him to stay, and transported him to Ramsey Abbey where he had once been a monk; he was allowed to spend the rest of his life there, dying in 1044.[3] Here, incidentally, is an example of the prejudiced view taken of leprosy, even by monks, towards a superior. In 1085, the Norman Hugh d'Orivalle, also a Bishop of London, died a leper. At the other end of the social

scale were the poor lepers sustained only by alms from the
charitable orders of the Church, and not even by this to any
extent before the twelfth century, and also the few wealthy
laymen who pitied them.

Much suffering was experienced by the leper, whether he
was of high or low station. Moreover, there was a tendency
to use the term 'leper' in an indiscriminate manner. When
Henry II issued his prohibition against bringing into the
country any document concerning the threatened papal
interdict, penalties were graded according to the rank of
individuals, the lowest rank being *leprosus*, clearly meaning
beggars or tramps.

There is some uncertainty about the epidemiology of
leprosy during the Middle Ages. Why, for instance, did its
incidence rise during the earlier centuries, only to fall
dramatically some four centuries or more later? And what
effect did the contemporary way of life have upon the
disease?

Diet was thought to have been a possible predisposing
factor. Salted meat and fish, often of poor quality and condition, incorrectly or carelessly cured pork, inferior grades of
bread made from contaminated barley or rye and similar
deficiencies in the supply of good, nutritious food, may well
have left the population at risk. The absence of vegetables,
particularly during the winter months, as well as poor
general living standards, would certainly reduce resistance to
disease and leave those who may perhaps have had a pre-
disposition to leprosy all the more liable to become its victims. Poverty, poor social conditions and lack of any real
hygienic sense would also help to advance the disease.

Like many diseases, leprosy requires a combination of
circumstances for it to flourish, but there seems to be some
evidence to suggest that, in addition to the specific organism
responsible, the long-term eating of rotten and putrid meat
and fish can give rise to conditions from which leprosy could
result.

We now know that the organism responsible for leprosy is

Mycobacterium leprae and its transmission is by close contact with a leprous patient for the causal bacteria can be found in the nasal secretions and in the saliva. The disease advances slowly but certainly, and from initial areas of anaesthesia, ulcers arise, which, together with neuritis and perhaps paralysis when untreated, can result in the destruction of both tissue and bone with consequent loss of the limb extremities.

With regard to the factors which were thought during the eleventh to fourteenth centuries to cause leprosy, these were principally contagion, having intercourse with a woman after she had been with a leprous man, heredity, and feeding a child with the milk of a leprous nurse.[4] Even the very breath or the glance of a leper could prove disastrous in the minds of the more gullible sections of the population!

The decline in its incidence was almost certainly due to the improvement in living conditions, however slight they may have been relative to later periods. Segregation, though nowhere near as complete as a superficial glimpse of the records might suggest, would also have some effect on reducing its contagious properties. Indeed, many of the legal requirements aimed at producing complete segregation had little effect, due to the difficulty of enforcing them. A further factor in its decline could well have been the gradual increase in bodily resistance shown by the population, who may have acquired a degree of immunity to the disease. This is a common reaction by populations after long-term contacts with an infectious disease.

That diet could play an important part in the causation of leprosy was suggested as long ago as Galen and, indeed, in the period under discussion, in the leper hospital at Sherburn near Durham, great care was taken to ensure that all the food given to the patients was fresh and wholesome. Bartolomeus Anglicus, in his treatise on leprosy (c 1230–50), warns of eating food that is 'corrupt or likely to be corrupt soon'.[5] John of Gaddesden (1314) also mentions 'errors of diet' as a cause of the disease in his medical work, the *Rosa Anglica*.[6]

K

It was to the great benefit of the leper that a favourable religious sentiment grew up and surrounded the sufferer, enabling him to seek and obtain some solace from the Church. Lepers were frequently referred to as *pauperes Christi* – Christ's poor – and there was an association with the biblical Lazarus: although there is no reason to suppose that he suffered from leprosy, his sanctity was none the less reflected on to the lepers to their considerable advantage. Also receiving benefit from this religious sentiment would be those suffering from the many other skin disorders mistakenly thought to be leprosy. All would be included in the medieval mind with 'Christ's poor'.

A notable example of this religious concern is that of Queen Matilda, wife of Henry I, who used to wash and kiss the feet of lepers, thereby considering she was carrying out her religious duties and charitable works.[7]

St Hugh of Lincoln likewise is said to have treated poor lepers and to have regarded them as the special protégés of Jesus. Here, however, some mistaken diagnosis has almost certainly been made. Hugh's biographer, Adam, states that the saint would wash the lepers' feet, give them alms and ensure their adequate maintenance. The afflicted would appear with 'swollen, livid and diseased faces, the eyes distorted or hollowed out and the lips wasted away'.[8] These symptoms refer more aptly to lupus, skin cancer or other tissue-destructive diseases than to leprosy, in which the lips and skin of the face become thickened and coarse rather than waste away.

This beneficial religious sentiment was by no means the only advantage enjoyed by the leper and it is significant that some people, particularly beggars, actually encouraged their neighbours to believe them to be sufferers from the disease in order to gain more pity and so be permitted to beg for alms, a privilege granted solely to lepers. They could also qualify for admission to a leper hospital whose standards, however rigorous, would be far above those to which they were accustomed. Moreover, whatever stigma may have been attached to the leper, his condition would be viewed with more compassion than that of the victim of venereal disease, for instance, especially to those holding high ecclesiastical office. Suffering from 'leprosy', therefore, could well have been considered preferable to being suspected of unethical or immoral behaviour.

For the average citizen, however, it was a serious matter to be regarded as a leper and considerable trouble was taken to ensure correct diagnosis. The general symptoms of the disease were well known and were copied by medical writers one from the other. Some of these writings show quite a detailed knowledge of the pathological processes: Gilbertus Anglicus (*c* 1230–40), for instance, correctly describes the loss of sensation affecting the fingers and toes which results in the typical mutilations of these extremities. This form of neuritis is even distinguished by him from the more general types of paralysis.[9] There must have been personal observation of actual cases of leprosy by Gilbertus, as there was also by a later physician, John of Gaddesden, who not only concerned himself with the symptoms but took the trouble to attempt a differential diagnosis. He wrote in his book the *Rosa Anglica*:

> No-one is to be adjudged a leper and isolated from all his fellows until the appearance and shape of his face be destroyed. And therefore 'cancer' in the feet and a foetid skin disease should not be taken as a proof of the disease even when accompanied by a nodular eruption, unless this be on the face. And because many are leprous before the appearance of these signs, be it known that there are three signs common to every form of leprosy.

By these three signs, John showed that he considered that the blood of lepers tended to be thicker and liable to more rapid clotting than is normal blood. He wrote:

> ... some of the blood is to be rubbed on the palms of the hand, and should it squeak or be more sticky than usual, this is a sign

of corruption. Secondly, take some blood and place it in very clear water, if it swim on the top, it is infected, but if it sink to the bottom, it is not so.

His third early diagnostic sign was to recommend that if three grains of salt were placed on some blood of the suspected person and the blood was affected, the salt would immediately dissolve.[10]

Excluding some of these curious beliefs, here is another example of the more detailed observations which were now beginning to be made in thirteenth-century medical practice. John even recognised that wasting of the first interosseus muscle of the hand took place and that the anaesthesia of the hands and feet presented a distribution that is now referred to as the 'glove and stocking' anaesthesia.

Bernard of Gordon (*c* late thirteenth century), in his medical text the *Lilium Medicinae*, makes a point of stressing the importance of correctly diagnosing the disease, though he doubts if his plea will be successful! Moreover, Gilbertus and Bernard both go into considerable detail when describing leprosy and are conscious of the fact that the anaesthesia of the hands and feet frequently results in the breaking down of the leprous sores into suppurating ulcers. Bartolomeus is aware also that ulcers, 'if they become chronic, they are messengers that foretell the peril of leprosy'. Deficient sensation or paraesthesia is described by both Gilbertus and Bernard, and this 'pins and needles' sensation is compared with the more total loss of sensation or anaesthesia, while Bartolomeus notes that 'feeling fails especially in most of the fingers'.

Gilbertus describes in minute detail how the eyebrows and eyelashes fall out, the nose and facial features become coarse, thickened and lumpy. The face, he noticed, loses the power of expression and the eyes appear unseeing. The voice becomes raucous and the limbs severely disfigured. While it is true that the descriptions of some of these symptoms have been copied from earlier writers such as the Arabic physician

Haly Abbas (*d* AD 994), his accurate detail is an advance on the writings of his predecessors.

In spite of this clear awareness by the physicians of the signs and symptoms of leprosy, it was not only to them that suspected cases went. Those afflicted could be examined by 'members of the clergy, civil officers or a jury of discreet men' in addition to medical practitioners.[11] In practice, the ordinary citizen would consult his parish priest as being probably the only literate person known to him. This is exemplified by the statement in a register of Bishop Bronescomb of Exeter: 'It belongs to the office of the priest to distinguish between one form of leprosy and another.'[12] What chance there was of correct diagnosis following such examinations by the clergy can only be surmised but one would imagine that the failure rate must have been considerable.

Once a leper was so diagnosed he would have to conform to certain legal requirements and, as we have indicated already, these were met by varying degrees of observance. A writ known as *De Leproso Amovendo* issued sometime before 1100 authorised the removal of a leper on account of the dangers from contagion. Yet even this document was not harshly enforced as can be seen from its wording, which strongly suggests that only if the leper proved an 'annoyance and disturbance' could the writ be applied. Moreover, unless his symptoms were very obvious, it would have been easy for a leper to roam the streets at will.

Most of the legislation concerning lepers was of a local character and, in the case of the city of London, the Assizes of 1276 laid down that 'no leper shall be in the city nor come there, nor make any stay there'. As with other laws relating to lepers, just how this could be enforced is not clear.

Yet all was by no means bleak or hopeless for the lepers. Because control over them was delegated to the local level, different attitudes could prevail in different places and at different times.

At Exeter, for example, lepers had for long been allowed to move about without restriction. The Bishop of Exeter, as early as 1163, had confirmed the right by which lepers could come to market twice a week to collect food and twice a week to collect alms, although by 1244 this freedom of movement was curtailed.

Among other similar examples of the help which was extended to those suffering from leprosy may be quoted the gift of King John to the lepers of Shrewsbury in 1204, of the right to a certain proportion of the flour sold in the market. In Chester, lepers were granted tolls from the sale of various foods, and even a cheese or a salmon was given from each load brought to market; while in Southampton, they received a penny for certain fixed amounts of wine imported through the town's docks.[13]

The general legal attitude to the English leper was undoubtedly tolerant as compared with that existing in other European countries. It would not be an unreasonable summary to quote the words of a thirteenth-century church law from Scotland which declared that lepers might even carry out their local duties, and 'if they cannot be induced to do so, let no coercion be employed, seeing that affliction should not be accumulated upon the afflicted, but rather their misfortunes commiserated'.[14]

Apart from the legal requirements concerning his person, the leper had to comply with those to do with his property. There seems to be some evidence to suggest that early legislation took away from the leper his right of inheritance but this appears to have fallen into disuse during the century following the Conquest, and certainly by the end of the thirteenth century leprous men were claiming and being awarded their inherited property.

It is of interest to describe here the religious service which, in theory at any rate, was to be observed when a leper was so classified. Just how much of this religious office was actually performed is hard to determine, but an order of service was nevertheless in existence, and it was clearly intended to be used even if only for guidance. After a ritual of being sprinkled with holy oil and kneeling under a black cloth, the leper went through a formalised *Responsum*. He was led from the church and, once outside, the priest declared the following prohibitions; some at least, as we have already seen, were not universally observed. He was forbidden to enter churches, go to market, mill or bakehouse or any assembly of people. He must not wash his hands or belongings in the local stream and, when he wished to drink, he must use his own cup. He must dress in his leper's clothes so as to be recognised and must always wear shoes. He could not enter an inn for wine unless it was poured directly into his cup, and he was not to have sexual relations with anyone other than his wife. He was forbidden to touch babies, or to give away any of his possessions. He could not eat in company unless they, too, were lepers. He was then enjoined to worship regularly and the service concluded with the priest instructing the leper to 'Worship God, and give thanks to God. Have patience and the Lord will be with thee. Amen.' It is unfortunate that we cannot tell just how much solace the leper may have acquired from this advice! When he died, the leper had his own chapel and churchyard reserved for him and his fellows. In fact, by a provision of the Lateran Council of 1179, it was authorised that lepers should have their own churches, cemeteries and the services of a priest.

In a leper cemetery at South Acre, Norfolk, for example, twelve burials were excavated dating from *c* 1100 to 1350. Out of the eight reasonably complete skeletons, the bones of seven displayed those pathological changes expected as a result of leprosy. In this case, it would seem that the leper house in which these individuals had lived did contain genuine lepers and that the diagnosis of the disease was generally accurate.

Noteworthy features shown by these skeletal remains were that each individual had at least one sinus resulting from discharging periodontal abscess cavities, probably due to the poor state of oral hygiene as a result of leprous spread into the mouth. There seems also to have been a low degree of dental attrition suggesting that the inmates were fed with soft, moist foods to protect their painful mouths from the normal, more abrasive diets.[15]

It is unfortunate that more evidence of leprosy from English skeletal material is not forthcoming for this is virtually the only account so far undertaken of the osteopathology of English lepers from the Middle Ages. It would be possible to determine with much more accuracy the incidence of leprosy in medieval England, if archaeologists were more aware of the bony indications for leprosy as, indeed, for many other diseases. In this way the present lack of knowledge of the rise and decline of leprosy in this country, for instance, might be overcome.

In order to be instantly recognised, these unfortunate people were expected to dress in a distinctive uniform. Contemporary pictures show the leper dressed in a cloak with a hood attached, a hat, plain shoes and carrying a bell or clappers to warn the public of his approach. In addition, he is sometimes shown carrying a begging bowl. Occasionally typical mutilations are faithfully recorded in these illustrations, which represent the victim with a wooden leg below the knee or perhaps the absence of some fingers or other extremities.

There is, in fact, one illustration in existence which gives a very good idea of how a contemporary saw the leper. It is an engraving on a seal from a document concerning the payment of rent between the Holy Innocent's Hospital in Lincoln and the Priory of Billington.[16] Dated during the reign of Henry II (1154–89), it shows a leper supported by two crutches, the left one placed in his armpit while the right crutch is placed under the right forearm to support it in an extended and begging position. This is interesting for the engraving could well be an accurate portrayal of the way a leper would need to support his arm, due to the paralysis which occurs as the disease progresses. The left leg below the knee is shown to be artificial, apparently made of wood, and here again is an accurate representation of a typical lower limb leprous deformity.

The leper then was compelled to exist as best he could, begging for alms, living wherever he could and relying utterly on the charity of neighbours while, no doubt, his condition deteriorated remorselessly and his appearance and deformities became ever more repulsive.

Was there nothing that man in the Middle Ages could do to counter the ravages and suffering arising from this dreadful disease? There were two avenues open to these unfortunate people: one was to be admitted to a leper hospital, and the second was to try out the uncertain and unpleasant 'cures' of the time, all of which were of little avail.

That these remedies were more or less useless is certain and Bartolomeus Anglicus tells us that leprosy 'is very hard to cure but by the help of God . . .'. He does recommend, however, that only fresh food be eaten, and that one should avoid food 'that overheats the blood' although he gives no indication of what these foods might be. Venesection or bloodletting might be attempted if the health of the patient was good enough, although Bartolomeus does warn that this procedure should be avoided if the patient is weak. Purging is also prescribed. The patient 'should use due medicines within and appropriate plasters and ointments without to withstand the complications', continues Bartolomeus, which sounds reasonable even if not particularly helpful, but he goes on to show that although in some directions a gleam of rational treatment was becoming apparent, there still remained a body of primitive and absurd ideas. For he proceeds: 'To heal leprosy or to hide it . . . the best remedy is a red adder with a white belly if the venom is away and the tail and the head smitten off. Then the body sodden with leeks should be taken and eaten often.'[17] While the remedies may indeed be absurd, it should be remembered that leprosy is even today a difficult disease to manage and treat effectively.

In addition to physicians' remedies, lepers took themselves

to places offering medicinal waters, and some of the leper hospitals were to be found near to such springs. Healing miracles are recorded as having taken place at some of these baths and wells and there are many claims of cures at the shrine of St Thomas of Canterbury.

Holy water made from a drop of St Thomas' blood, frequently diluted from a well in the crypt of the cathedral, was used for the cure. Some cases improved while the leper remained at Canterbury only to relapse when he returned home, while others were claimed as permanent cures. For instance, Benedict, a monk of Canterbury and an eyewitness to some of these miraculous 'cures', and William of Canterbury, a custodian of the shrine who was also a witness, tell the story of a leper named Randulf of Langton who had found himself compelled to make arrangements for admission to a leper house. He visited the tomb of St Thomas, prayed, wept, and made vows. He stayed nine days in Canterbury, using the holy water, both internally and externally, and began to improve sufficiently to go home. At the end of a month he came back, apparently cured. We are told that subsequently he went on a pilgrimage to Jerusalem. However, by the time of his return his leprosy had recurred, even worse than before. Here indeed is an unusual example of clerical honesty!

A further story is given by these two monks about one Gerard who was afflicted with leprosy but who managed to remain in his home town due to his popularity with his fellow citizens (no enforced segregation here). Eventually, however, when he was preparing to go into a leper hospital, Gerard is said to have had a vision of himself lying prostrate at the martyr's tomb, while the saint breathed through a gap in the tomb directed into Gerard's mouth. So directed, he travelled to Canterbury where he spent nine days drinking and annointing himself with the mixture of blood and water. He departed after securing some abatement in the disease, returning later to show everyone that he was fully cured of his affliction.

A final example, and again one of failure, is that of Gilbert of St Valery, who was only ten years old when he was brought to the shrine because of his leprosy. After only three days, the sores and ulcerations disappeared and sensation was restored to his hands and feet. He seemed to be well on the way to recovery, but sadly, on his return home, he soon relapsed and became even more severely afflicted than before.[18]

How many of these stories refer to genuine leprosy can never be determined, nor can one comprehend what pathological changes may have occurred in the condition of these people. The significant factor in all these 'miracles' is the strong belief which was maintained during the entire medieval period (and is even now not entirely disbelieved) that they *could* happen and indeed many 'cures' were expected to occur as a matter of course. It is more than probable that on the strength of a few apparent cures of people suffering from hysterical conditions, the shrine would become swamped with sick pilgrims. They would all be more than willing to donate contributions in the name of the martyr and so the shrine and its guardians, however scrupulous, would most certainly benefit both spiritually and materially. This is not to say that cures were never obtained, but in the contemporary religious atmosphere the expectation of a cure became the seed which grew and flowered into the strong belief of its reality. This expectation would be encouraged by those whose position may well have depended upon the continuation of such miraculous happenings.

LEPER HOSPITALS

As the incidence of leprosy slowly increased and the problem of the leper became more acute, society felt the need to do something about the care of its victims. In addition to purely humanitarian reasons, there was the fear of contagion, and the necessity in the medieval mind to avoid the sight of the grotesque disfigurement of the lepers. Along with these, other purely practical considerations such as the need to house lepers and keep them from roaming the streets uncontrolled, played their part in the foundation of leper hospitals, or lazar houses, as they were called.

The disease seems to have reached its peak during the twelfth century, for during its second half more leper hospitals were founded than in any other period. At the end of that century the rate of increase slowed down, until by about 1400, when the disease seems virtually to have disappeared, there were no further hospitals being built for lepers; indeed, many were by that time already in use for other purposes. As early as 1342, the leper hospital at Ripon reported that it had no more inmates being admitted, so its funds were redirected to provide dole for the general poor; in 1348 the large leper house at St Albans contained only two or three patients, and by 1361 the hospitals of St John and St Leonard at Aylesbury were actually in ruins.[19]

The leper hospitals were not always used exclusively for the care of the leper; they could admit also various other aged, sick and infirm people. Sometimes elderly monks might end their days in such a house, as also might those fallen upon hard times. The common feature of most, though not all, of these establishments was the religious supervision and discipline under which their inmates lived.

Moreover, of those houses which were founded solely for lepers, some admitted only certain classes of society. For instance, the hospital at Walsingham in Norfolk was reserved for wealthy lepers with good family connections, while that of St Laurence at Canterbury was intended for the use of the clergy.[20]

The earliest known hospitals founded for lepers were two built by Archbishop Lanfranc (1070–89). One dedicated to St John was established at Canterbury, being built of stone. This hospital was not confined to lepers, but was intended also for the poor, infirm, lame and blind suffering from 'several diseases'; it was so described to distinguish it from a foundation caring solely for lepers. The other, St Nicholas's, which was built of wood and specifically for the leprous, was at Harbledown near Canterbury. A charter of Henry II confirming the hospital's endowments describes its patients as 'leprosi'. This hospital originally catered for both men and women, but by 1164 a women's house was established at Thanington, just south of Canterbury, to accommodate twenty-five leprous women. It was served by a master, a prioress and three priests, a strong indication of the religious nature of these houses. Another early leper house, founded in 1137, and intended for monks, was that of St Laurence, also at Canterbury; and even earlier, sometime before 1108, St Bartholomew's was erected at Rochester, Kent.

Before the first half of the twelfth century was over, numerous establishments were founded all over the country. Whitby, Oxford, Newcastle, Bury St Edmunds, Warwick, Lancaster, Norwich, Dover, York and Northampton are examples of the wide distribution of these houses as the twelfth century progressed. It has been calculated that by the end of the century, Norfolk had no fewer than twenty leper hospitals, while Norwich alone had six.[21] No doubt this large number of houses was connected with the general prosperity of the region; East Anglia was one of the richest parts of England at this time. It has been further estimated that in the first half of the twelfth century out of at least 46 hospitals founded, 24 were for lepers; in the remaining fifty years of the century, 120 hospitals were established of which 56 were for leper patients. In the thirteenth century, however, out of 240 hospitals, only 75 were endowed for lepers.[22] Here is an early indication, if these figures can be relied upon, of the decreasing need for specific accommodation for leprous patients which, as we have seen, was to continue into the fourteenth century.

It is noteworthy that although these numbers seem high, they are considerably lower than those for the continent during the same period, which suggests that England suffered less from leprosy than did the mainland of Europe.

In London, a similar pattern can be seen. An early hospital

was St Giles's, founded by Queen Matilda, wife of Henry I, in 1101, and intended to be supported by donations from the citizens. It was designed to accommodate forty patients. A second was St James's, Westminster (*c* 1150), established to provide for the care of fourteen women rather strangely referred to as 'young lepers'; it has only recently been recognised that children are highly susceptible to leprosy. Was it perhaps even then realised that young people were at high risk and should be cared for together?

It was perhaps in this field of caring for those afflicted with leprosy that the private benefactor or patron became most active. It has already been shown how leading persons of the time made it their business to care for these people: royalty like Queen Matilda, and great ecclesiastical figures such as St Hugh of Lincoln and Archbishop Lanfranc. During the twelfth century, these provisions were extended by individual patrons of lesser degree, who endowed and supported leper hospitals and ensured their maintenance by granting contributions while they lived and by provision in their wills when they died. Monasteries also established similar hospitals and, in the case of St Albans Abbey, two houses were founded and maintained by it. The first, built in 1146 by Abbot Gregory (1119–46) and named after St Julian, was intended to accommodate six brethren. It fell on hard times, however, due to taxation by the Crown, and the inmates were not well cared for. The second was established for women by Abbot Warin in 1194 and was dedicated to St Mary de Pré. Later, in common with many such establishments, it became inhabited by poor and needy nuns as the number of leprous patients declined.[23]

Another example of a private patron was the Earl of Chester who in about 1181 established a hospital at Coventry for local lepers. Henry I before 1135 endowed the hospital of the Holy Innocents at Lincoln to accommodate ten patients. In this case also, the gradual run-down in the number of lepers is noted, for by the mid-fourteenth century only one leper patient remained.

Archbishop Thurston of York, some time before his death in 1139, founded a leper hospital at Ripon intended for the care of eighteen inmates.

It has already been indicated that some hospitals catered for various kinds of patient, leprosy being just one of several diseases cared for. For instance, at the hospital of St Mary Magdalen at Kings Lynn, Norfolk, founded in 1145, there was provision for 'whole' patients as well as for lepers. St Leonard's at Lancaster, founded by Prince John in 1189, was similarly intended for the benefit of sufferers from various illnesses in addition to leprosy.

John, incidentally, seems to have had some sympathy for his leper subjects, for he provided considerable resources for their care. In 1207–8, for example, at Bristol, he granted the lepers of the town a settlement outside the gates where they could live under his protection and were allowed to beg in safety.[24] This is an interesting example of care being provided by a non-ecclesiastical authority. Similarly at Norwich there were four shelters placed under the direction of a lay-keeper and supported by contributions from the town's citizens and travellers, and at Lynn there were three secular houses under lay supervision, but these were founded much later, in about 1432.

Further examples of hospitals which would admit diseases other than leprosy were St Bartholomew's at Oxford, founded in 1126 by Henry I, and Norman's Spital at Norwich, which catered for both 'whole sisters and half sisters'.

In 1181, the Bishop of Durham endowed a large leper hospital at Sherburn outside the city to accommodate up to sixty-five people of both sexes. Another monastic patron was the Abbey of Barking which in 1180 founded a lazar house at Ilford for its tenants and servants; this could cater for thirteen patients.

It is almost impossible to determine among the many hospitals and similar institutions of the period those concerned solely with leprosy, due both to the persistently loose use of the term 'leper' and to the fact that references, especially in the later records to leper or lazar houses cannot be relied upon to provide anything other than generalised information. For these reasons, it is not possible to form an accurate picture of the geographical distribution of leper hospitals in medieval England.

There is evidence, however, of how the lepers were treated in these hospitals and under what regulations they lived. As has already been seen, most of these houses were relatively small in size and conducted themselves on strictly ecclesiastical lines. Some of these shelters, indeed, required married men to separate from their wives if they were to be admitted, and if the leper was a woman, it was required that she take vows to become a nun.

Each hospital imposed its own regulations on its inmates and they were expected to conform to such rules as were applied and to dress in the manner laid down. When one recalls that these unfortunate sufferers would have been dressed in little more than rags and at the mercy of society's charity for both food and clothing, the advantages of admission to one of these institutions with their orderly routine and regular provision of the necessities of life will be apparent.

Either the patients could be admitted on the recommendation of the patron, or the keeper or brother in charge could agree to accept the applicant. Once admitted, the leper was given certain rights as well as duties. At the Sherburn house at Durham, the rules allowed the patients to be visited by friends and, moreover, if any of these visitors had come from long distances, they could be accommodated for the night.[25] Here is another indication of the recognition that short periods of contact did not usually result in the spread of the disease. There seems to have been a distinct difference of opinion on this: on the one hand we have seen how the belief existed that even the sight of a leper or his touch was enough to transmit the disease, and on the other we find that visitors were prepared not only to visit the patient but to stay the night under the same roof.

It would seem that living in these hospitals was considered a privilege for, in return for the comfort, safety, rights bestowed, food and clothing and other benefits, some duties were imposed. In particular, the duty of obedience was expected, for the records show that for any inmate whose behaviour was such that neither punishment by flogging nor a diet of bread and water was sufficient to mend his ways, then the final sanction of expulsion would be applied.[26] The thought of having to leave and face the cruel world alone again would check all but the most recalcitrant inmates.

In some establishments the lepers themselves could approve or reject the admission of a new patient, or could nominate someone to fill a vacancy. On admission, they would renounce all their personal possessions, and any charity or alms collected outside had to be put into the communal treasury. In general no trading of any kind was permitted, and the patient's clothing and personal furniture were all that he was allowed to retain.

Different houses permitted or prohibited different activities. Some allowed their inmates to move outside relatively freely, others might permit entry only to certain places outside while still others might forbid such entry. Some lepers were not allowed out on their own, whereas others could travel long distances for compassionate family reasons.

It should not be thought, however, that these rules and regulations were in any way imposed because of the nature of the disease. They were largely a matter of house discipline, and similar controls were imposed upon inmates of many alms-houses and other non-leper institutions for the poor and infirm.

Discipline was maintained in the leper hospitals by the imposition of severe punishments. At Reading a leper who committed an offence had to live on bread and water, his normal rations of more acceptable food being divided among his brethren. In Exeter, in addition to offenders being compelled to fast on bread and water, they were put into the stocks, and such punishments could well last for many days

L

if the offence was thought to warrant it. A month's punishment would be imposed for violence, and for lesser offences the warden was not slow to use his cane for flogging.[27]

The warden or master of a leper house could himself be a leper and at St Leonard's at Lancaster, the master was elected from the ranks of the lepers themselves; some hospitals could have both a leprous and a healthy master simultaneously and others could have a leper master only if they so desired it. Most houses had some staff free from the disease, who would be employees of the hospital in the normal way. At Sherburn there were servants employed in the laundry and also to look after those patients confined to their beds. Except for bedridden cases, the inmates were expected to hear mass and perform other religious offices regularly at the canonical hours by day and night. Even those in bed were required to join in these acts of worship or, at least, pray by themselves.

With regard to life inside the hospital, it remains only to comment upon the general care which would normally be offered to its inmates. Food standards would vary enormously, from the sparse food of poor quality available in the smaller leper settlement depending solely on charitable alms, to the regular and adequate diet available in large and well-endowed institutions like those at Sherburn, Harbledown and Thanington. At Sherburn each patient was given a loaf of bread and a gallon of beer daily, meat was given three times a week, and eggs, fish, cheese, butter and vegetables were provided regularly. Many leper hospitals emphasised the importance of fresh food, and rotting meat, fish and stale bread were forbidden.

For the comfort of the inmates, provision was made for fires; wood, peat and other fuels were granted to the patients. Since cleanliness was generally considered important in the care of the leper, baths were made available and patients were expected to keep their hair and bodies clean and their clothes properly washed.

These examples illustrate that though the leper was

shunned, segregated (in varying degrees of severity), taken from his family and friends, lost much of his property, and suffered from the most gruesome and severe mutilations and deformities, on the other hand he did have the benefit of custodial care in the leper house. Even if the standards, hopes and rules of the founders were not always achieved or maintained and the leper was made to observe a rigorous regime, nevertheless he was offered a life of shelter, warmth and a degree of comfort which was the envy of many of his more healthy contemporaries.

An opportunity was thus given to those suffering people to congregate together for some mutual comfort and protection in the face of the almost overwhelming hostility shown them by much of society and the total lack of any medical assistance to help them overcome the ravages of their disease.

7

The Monastic Infirmary

The care of its sick, aged and infirm was a responsibility laid upon the monastic community early in the development of the communal religious life. In fact, very early in our period, Bede tells the story of Caedmon, the seventh-century poet of the monastery at Whitby, who ended his days in an infirmary to which he had retired.[1]

The rule of St Benedict specifically required that sick brethren were to be given every consideration and assistance and great pains were taken to ensure the recovery of sick monks. Moreover, this rule, which was to become the model of most subsequent monastic rules, contains only three examples where the words 'above all' are used for emphasis: one of these concerns the care of the sick (Chapter 36). This chapter commences,

> Before all things and above all things, care must be taken of the sick, so that they may be served in very deed as Christ himself . . . Therefore let the abbot take the greatest care that they [the sick] suffer no neglect. For these sick brethren let there be assigned a special room and an attendant who is God fearing, diligent and careful . . . Let the abbot take the greatest care that the sick be not neglected by the cellarers and attendants; for he must answer for all misdeeds of his disciples.[2]

Further sections of St Benedict's rule insist that whatever

is required for the care of sick monks must be properly and adequately provided. For instance, in section 31, the cellarer is clearly made responsible for, amongst other things, 'the greatest care of the sick, of children, of guests and of the poor', while section 48 makes allowances for the sick and delicate in the daily round of physical labour.

While it is certain that considerable attention and devotion were given to those who fell ill, it is equally certain that the principles by which the sick were treated were strictly in accordance with the prevailing view that much illness was divinely ordained for the punishment of sin. Those who suffered were attended to and efforts were made to provide cures, but the whole concept of healing was subordinate to religious practice and doctrine. The cure of the soul took precedence over the cure of the body. Despite this limitation, however, monastic provision for the sick gradually developed until eventually nearly all monasteries of any size had their own infirmary and staff; indeed some of the larger Cistercian establishments possessed two infirmaries, one for the monks and one for the lay brothers, the *conversi*.

The monastic infirmary was normally one of a group of buildings used by the sick and often lay to the east of the great cloister away from any noise and disturbance. There were variations in the location of the infirmary, taking account of the many architectural and topographical features which made uniformity of building impossible, not to mention the different building requirements of different religious orders.

The infirmary was intended not only for the care and treatment of the sick, but also for use as living quarters for elderly and delicate monks who would thereby be excused the normal vigorous routine of the community, a great boon for the aged in a world not oversensitive to the welfare of the old and work-worn.

The infirmary itself consisted of a hall wherein the patients' beds were situated, a chapel attached to it, a kitchen and a frater or dining hall where the eating of meat was permitted. Some monasteries in addition had an infirmary cloister to provide a covered walk for exercise, a garden for the cultivation of herbs and plants and apartments for the specific use of the Infirmarian or master of the infirmary.

The hall, or ward as it would now be called, was rectangular and sometimes of considerable size; when a chapel was present, it would be frequently attached to the east side of the hall. At Fountains Abbey, for example, the infirmary hall measured 180ft by 78ft, and at Christ Church, Canterbury, the hall length was as much as 237ft from east to west.[3]

There were two main types of infirmary hall, the open plan and the aisled plan. In an aisled plan hall, the room or ward was divided by arcading into three areas or alleys, rather like a nave and aisles in a church. In the aisles were placed the beds, arranged at right angles to the walls as is now the custom in hospital. Occasionally this pattern was changed, for at Furness the beds were placed in alcoves parallel to the walls.[4] Light was admitted to the hall by windows situated in the walls above the beds in the aisle-less or open-plan chamber or by windows in the celestory in the case of the aisled hall. Fireplaces provided the means of heating and three or more fires were often lit in the hall.

As time went on, there was a tendency to provide some privacy and sub-division of the hall began to take place. Cubicles were surrounded by curtains at first, then wood and stone partitions were built until eventually many later infirmaries possessed separate single-bedded rooms. This type of partitioning took place at Meaux and Canterbury at the end of the fourteenth century and at Fountains, Kirkstall and Waverley in about 1500. As the fifteenth century progressed, the practice of sub-division became the normal form of accommodation.

In Cistercian foundations, the infirmary was often situated farther away from the main cloister than was the case with other orders, and covered infirmary passages were built to connect the infirmary to the eastern part of the main range of buildings. Fountains, Kirkstall, Rievaulx, Jervaulx and Furness all had covered passages and some even possessed branch passages leading off to the church.

The kitchen was a small building frequently situated at the side of the infirmary hall. Here was cooked the more nourishing food; and meat, forbidden to the healthy members of the community, could be prepared for the patients. Adjoining the kitchen was the infirmary frater or dining room, also called the *misericord*. This was used by ambulant patients and was also the place where relaxations in diet were permitted. The name originated from the word *misericordia* meaning indulgence and, because meat was allowed only to the sick, the *misericord* was naturally attached to the infirmary buildings. However, as the consumption of meat became more general due to relaxations in monastic diet during the thirteenth century and after, the use of the *misericord* became less obvious and it was, in fact, built adjoining the main frater at the monasteries of Jervaulx and Kirkstall, thus becoming available to the whole community.

Mention has been made of the rooms under the general responsibility of the master of the infirmary and some idea of their use can be deduced from a surviving plan of the ninth-century Anglo-Irish monastery of St Gall, Switzerland. It is not known if this plan was ever executed entirely, but it may be reasonably assumed to reflect the ideal in ninth-century monastic practice. It contains a section devoted to the infirmary and its adjoining buildings and is extremely comprehensive in its provision for the sick. Bathrooms, warm rooms with fireplaces, a ward specially intended for serious cases and blood-letting rooms are all provided, in addition to those normally present as detailed above. A physician was evidently expected to take charge for he is allotted a house, a consulting room, and a drug store or dispensary, while a large herb garden is laid out containing sixteen named herbs, presumably those most in demand at the time.

The physician's house is surrounded by the ward for serious cases, the dispensary and his consulting room, thereby

affording the doctor maximum convenience. Among the
herbs shown in the plan are rose, mustard, fennel, lily, sage,
mint, pennyroyal and rosemary. A gardener would probably
have been employed to cultivate the plants under the
guidance of the physician or Infirmarian. On the west side of
the physician's house is the blood-letting and purging room,
north of which lies a group of water closets for the use of the
inmates.

Drains and water-courses were often constructed through
which water from a nearby stream would flow, so removing
refuse and excrement. These water-courses, sometimes stone
lined, are a frequent feature still to be seen in surviving ruins.

The patient in a monastic infirmary would clearly be subjected to differing standards of treatment according to the
order and its financial assets. At the Augustinian Priory at
Barnwell, Cambridgeshire, towards the end of the thirteenth
century, great indulgence was shown to the sick and one of
the abbot's duties was to ensure that the 'Master of the
Farmery', the Infirmarian, was 'to be always at hand to
wait upon the sick man, that he may want for nothing to
relieve his infirmity or his suffering . . .'.[5]

In stark contrast is the view of St Bernard of Clairvaux,
who considered it 'unbefitting religion and contrary to
simplicity of life' for Cistercian monks to buy drugs, take
medicines or visit doctors. Further, the Carthusians would
not even allow their sick monks to obtain the services of a
physician at any time and infirmary buildings were not
permitted in their monasteries. Carthusians lived and died
in their own cells or apartments.

The sick monks at Barnwell were regarded as having fallen
into three main groups. The first were those whose health
had broken down due to overwork, fatigue, sleeplessness,
long periods of silence and other irksome features of their
life. The mental malaise resulting from these causes was
recognised as being inappropriate for the available medicines
and so rest and comfort was recommended. Quiet walks in
the fields and meadows were suggested and the sick were

allowed to take their meals with the monks undergoing venesection. A change of air and scenery with adequate exercise was evidently acknowledged as being beneficial in these cases.

The second group of sick monks included those suffering from the common everyday ailments: fevers, toothache, 'gouty spasms', eye complaints, throat, spleen and liver disorders and 'pains in diverse parts of the body'.[6] These monks had to apply for admission to the infirmary where the Infirmarian was to treat them with care and devotion. A physician could be called in if necessary, possibly even a lay practitioner, and various treatments were available including baths which were normally forbidden outside the infirmary. The Observance implies that the Infirmarian was not himself a physician but more of a nursing attendant, expected to deal only with milder cases. In serious illness a physician was to be called in.

As soon as their health improved, the patients were expected to return to their normal duties and were not to remain in the infirmary enjoying the special diets available there.

The third class of sick monks at Barnwell were those who had suffered acute attacks of illness such as paralysis, stroke or sudden attacks of severe pain or perhaps serious accidental injury. These patients were naturally not expected to ask permission to be admitted to the infirmary, but were to be taken there immediately. In these serious cases the patients 'may eat, drink, talk and sleep at whatever hours and so often as they find convenient, for no rule is imposed upon patients of this class'.[7] It is significant that some emphasis is placed upon the abbot's duty of visiting these patients to care for their souls, suggesting the frequency with which such illnesses proved fatal.

A somewhat more rigorous regime for the sick was prescribed by Archbishop Lanfranc in his eleventh-century *Monastic Constitutions*. If a brother became ill, he had to prostrate himself in chapter and, when permitted to rise,

had to confess his inability to carry out his normal duties. He
was then advised to 'treat yourself as your sickness demands
and stay away from conventual duties at your discretion'.[8]

Should his condition deteriorate, he would be allowed into
the infirmary and, if permitted to eat meat, had to wear his
hood over his head and use a staff when walking. When he
recovered, he was expected to publicly ask for pardon for 'I
have offended in matters of food and drink and much
else . . .'.[9]

It seems, therefore, that monastic authorities provided, for
their time, a reasonable standard of care for the sick and aged
and monks admitted to the infirmaries were granted many
concessions and indulgences, a more nourishing and varied
diet and the best available medical treatment and supervision.

This treatment and medical care was the responsibility of
the master of the infirmary, who had specific religious as
well as medical duties and was in charge of a staff of assistants
called *infirmarii*. The duties expected of the Infirmarian were
quite definite and in both Lanfranc's *Monastic Constitutions*
and the *Customs and Observances* at Barnwell, clear instructions
are laid down as to what was required of him. Lanfranc instructs the Infirmarian to personally serve the meals to his
patients even if they have been cooked by an assistant. He is
expected to sprinkle holy water daily over the beds of the
sick and various prayers are to be recited. Of particular importance for the Infirmarian is the instruction that 'he shall
take a dark lantern and go round the beds of all the sick,
seeing carefully that no-one who is capable of rising shall
remain in bed. It is his special duty to disclose and accuse in
chapter the negligences of all who abide in the foremen-
tioned infirmary.'[10] No doubt malingering was not unknown
within the community, for much the same reasons as blood-
letting was used, to procure relaxations and indulgences. In
fact, music, normally forbidden, could be heard in the
privacy of the chapel if it was felt that it might uplift the
patients.

Although Lanfranc's *Constitutions* leave an impression of strictness, he does impose upon the abbot the responsibility that 'nothing necessary for the infirmarian's office shall ever be lacking in the infirmary'.[11]

At Barnwell, the master of the infirmary was expected to be gentle, compassionate and good-tempered, willing to help the sick at all times. He was also allowed an assistant who was to be on continuous duty serving meals, helping the physician when he was examining patients' urine and generally looking after the sick. He was also expected to be trustworthy, sober and of a placid nature for he would often have to hear patients' secrets. He was also expected to endure all the nasty and distasteful aspects of his work without complaint and under the direction of his superior prepare the dead for burial.

The Infirmarian was to have mass celebrated daily for the benefit of his patients while prayers and readings were also to be recited. Women were never to enter the infirmary, nor was any secular person to do so without permission. Physicians, however, could take meals with their patients when on visits.[12]

It would seem that conditions were relatively easier for the inmates at Barnwell's infirmary than for those observing Lanfranc's Rule. The care of the sick generally had evidently improved during the two hundred years between the time of Lanfranc and when Barnwell flourished. Indeed, at St Albans in Abbot Geoffrey's time (1119–46), the Infirmarian was required to prepare a daily report upon the condition of his patients.[13] Furthermore, at Abingdon, the Infirmarian was expected to sleep in the infirmary and be responsible for the keys. Any monk wishing to visit the infirmary had to be escorted there and back; such were the strict rules of access. The Infirmarian was also responsible for the provision of candles, wood and fuel in cold weather and bowls and towels for washing, while the wash places themselves had to be kept in good repair.[14]

During the eleventh to thirteenth centuries, the monasteries were beginning to train their own physicians whose duties were mainly, though not exclusively, the care of the monastic community. They did attend to patients outside the walls of their monasteries and some were much sought after as their skill became widely known. Equally they were available to help the sick who came into the monasteries for medical advice and the monastic infirmary gradually became more available to the laity. Several monasteries even possessed separate infirmaries for use by the neighbouring general population. A patient from one infirmary could also be transferred to another if it was thought that more skilled attention was available.[15]

Some monk physicians reached the very highest levels in society and royal service. Those who attended the nobility and the rich quickly came into contact with luxurious living and slackness in monastic discipline soon resulted, until several papal prohibitions were published in the early twelfth century, forbidding monk physicians to practice their craft for fees. That they were so skilled is not surprising when it is remembered that the quiet and tranquillity of a monastery would have produced the ideal conditions under which the practice of medicine could be studied and the art of healing practised. In addition they were ideal places for the copying and reading of medical texts.

The monastic infirmaries were expected to keep a supply of medicines and it was, no doubt, in their herb gardens that many of the herbs required for the preparation of medicines were grown. Such ingredients as peony, ginger, cinnamon and balsam were expected to be always available to comfort the sick. These seem to have been highly regarded as medicinal ingredients to be so specifically mentioned in the records. Moreover, monastic financial accounts show that sums of money were frequently expended on such items as aniseed, wine, cassis, cloves, saxifrage, liquorice, olive oil, vinegar and scammany.[16]

To compensate the monasteries in some degree for the expenditure of resources on the care of the sick, contributions were received from people anxious to ensure their admission to an infirmary in their old age: an early attempt at insurance! Further revenues were forthcoming from pilgrims and penitents who donated money to houses of the poor and sick. Rents and food from land as well as property owned by a monastery were sometimes earmarked for the benefit of the infirmary. Other income came from royal grants paid by sheriffs from profits accruing from Crown lands. The *Pipe Rolls* record many examples of moneys paid to hospitals in all parts of the country.

MONASTIC PHYSICIANS

A fruitful and indispensable source for the identity and activities of monk physicians are the monastic chronicles which record persons and events thought important enough to merit inclusion in the local records of the monasteries. A few examples of these physicians will be referred to from a selection of the principal surviving chronicles.

Abbot Baldwin, already noted in chapter 4, was a very well-known physician in his time. As well as acting as personal physician to both Edward the Confessor and William the Conqueror, he was called in to attend to many eminent people and frequently travelled to the continent on medical business. William of Malmesbury testifies that Baldwin was sent to Bury St Edmunds in 1065 to help Abbot Leofstan who was then suffering from paralysis of his hands, thought to have been the result of gout. He was unsuccessful, but made such a favourable impression that when Leofstan died later that year, Baldwin was elected to succeed him.[17] Archbishop Lanfranc was a patient of Baldwin and he is thought to have been one of the physicians present at the death of the Conqueror in 1087. Baldwin died about 1097.

Faritius, the distinguished physician of Abingdon monastery, was also an abbot who came from Italy some time before 1078. It is therefore possible that he had attended the medical school at Salerno. By 1100, he held ecclesiastical office at Malmesbury and his medical skill was already held in high esteem.[18] He was also the principal physician when Queen Matilda, wife of Henry I, gave birth to her first child in 1101. The chronicle of Abingdon records that Faritius was assisted at the queen's confinement by another Italian physician, Grimbald.[19] Henry I had such confidence in his abilities that Faritius was permitted to attend the king alone without any further assistance.[20] Abingdon greatly benefited from Faritius's reputation, for land was donated in appreciation of his services. He was held in such high regard by Henry that the king specifically exempted the abbot from paying the feudal aid in 1110 when his daughter Mathilda was betrothed to the Emperor Henry.

Ironically, Faritius's medical reputation was to impede his chances of succeeding Anselm as Archbishop of Canterbury in 1109. King Henry supported Faritius's candidature, but several bishops opposed him, regarding it as improper that a man famed for his treatment of women's disorders should be elected to such a high office.[21]

William of Malmesbury records yet another well-known physician, Gregory, who practised in the abbey at Malmesbury. Ernulf, father-in-law of Mathilda, the daughter of Henry I, had been suffering from some disease of the hands, gradually losing their use. He was advised to go to Malmesbury to consult Gregory, but to no avail. Geoffrey, the Abbot of Malmesbury, then found some balsam in the tomb of St Aldhelm which, when rubbed into Ernulf's hands, successfully cured him.[22]

A remarkable story is recorded in Matthew Paris's chronicle about a physician called Adam, Abbot at Croxton monastery in Leicestershire. He was present at the death of King John at Newark, having evidently been called in to attend to the king. As John had wished for burial at Worcester, Adam performed an operation to remove the king's organs and preserve them in salt. In this way, he considered that the body would be in a more suitable condition for travel while he had the organs buried in his own abbey.[23]

Nor was this the only time such a procedure was followed. Roger of Hoveden testifies that after the death of Henry I in Normandy, his organs, brain and eyes were removed and buried, the remainder of the body being cut into pieces and salted. However, in spite of this attempt at preservation, decomposition set in long before the body was returned to England for burial at Reading.[24]

Another monk physician of high reputation was Warin, Abbot of St Albans (1183–95). He had studied at Salerno and took a great deal of trouble to help leprous monks and nuns. He established the female leper hospital of St Mary de Pré in 1194 and made his monastery responsible for its maintenance.[25] As already noted in chapter 5, Warin permitted considerable latitude to those undertaking bloodletting and his sincere concern for the sick is apparent.

The St Albans chronicle further states that Warin's successor as abbot was John of Cella (1195–1214), also a physician, who was fortunate enough to have been compared to Galen. He appears to have been particularly skilled in the art of diagnosis from urine and he even predicted his own death from such an examination.[26] It is interesting to note that at this time there was at least one other medical practitioner attached to St Albans monastery, for it is recorded that a physician named William was called in to assist John in his own urine diagnosis.

Monastic physicians could earn considerable sums of money from their practices as can be seen from the example of Walter, the physician at Bury St Edmunds. He contributed large sums of money to help in the erection of a new almonry.[27]

When the various monastic chronicles are searched, there are many names associated with the practice of medicine and while practitioners in the larger monasteries like Abingdon and St Albans are better documented, it is clear that large numbers of conscientious and skilled physicians worked in the many monastic infirmaries during the twelfth and thirteenth centuries.

As the fourteenth century progresses, records of monastic

physicians become much more rare. The lay physician, with more freedom of movement and action, was now coming into his own. He was not only offering his services to the general public and in the secular hospitals now being established, but would also be called in to the serious cases in the monasteries. The monk physicians were also no doubt facing the difficulties arising from the various papal prohibitions of the late thirteenth and fourteenth centuries upon the practice of their craft. While these instructions may well have been overlooked on many occasions, they would have had an inhibiting effect over the years, so dissuading monks from embarking upon a medical career.

'SECULAR' HOSPITALS

One of the main difficulties in any discussion or review of non-monastic medieval hospitals is to determine which of them were hospitals in the modern meaning of the word and which were more likely to have been hostels, alms houses or other shelters for the poor. The following account is limited to those establishments whose principal function was the care of the sick and infirm.

While these hospitals could be considered secular in that they catered for the wider population, they were still maintained and administered in an ecclesiastical atmosphere. This religious nature is reflected in the great number of hospitals dedicated to saints and other Christian associations. Corpus Christi, Holy Ghost, Holy Trinity, St Edmund and St Thomas of Canterbury were all common hospital dedications.

The earliest known establishments were used mainly as alms houses or places where travellers could be accommodated. Gradually buildings more specifically intended for the sick were founded, though even these were used more for custodial care than for any active treatment of the acutely sick. Indeed, many of the smaller establishments could not have maintained any trained medical staff. Furthermore, very many of these 'hospitals' founded during the years 1100–1300 were designed to accommodate the poor and aged, or retired clergy and nuns, as much as the infirm and sick.

The earliest hospital is traditionally thought to have been St Peter's at York, founded about 936 with the help of King Athelstan. In 1135 it was re-founded under the Augustinian rule and became one of the largest hospitals in the country.

Another early hospital, at Flixton in Yorkshire, founded about 940, was intended for poor travellers and pilgrims as well as for the care of the sick, but a more specialised hospital was founded by Bishop Wulfstan at Worcester about 1085.

As in the case of leper houses, hospitals also catered for special classes of inmate. Some admitted only clerical patients, some limited themselves to one sex only while still others admitted only aged persons of various classes.

The geographical spread of hospitals was steadily extended and it has been estimated that the number of such institutions increased from about ten to twenty during the years 1066–1100 to some three to four hundred in the second half of the thirteenth century.[28] Many of these hospitals, however, had a short life and quickly ceased to exist altogether or were used for quite different purposes; many were adopted as shelters and alms houses.

An early establishment about which more is known than its mere existence was that founded by Archbishop Lanfranc in about 1087 at Canterbury. This hospital, St John's, Northgate, was, unusually for this time, built of stone and divided into two, one part to accommodate each sex. Lanfranc provided clothing and daily food, and attendants and guardians were appointed to care for the patients. To supervise their spiritual welfare, he erected a church staffed by canons who would visit the sick and, in the event of death, ensure that the patients had a proper burial.[29]

In 1123, St Bartholomew's in Smithfield, London, was founded by Rahere, a courtier of Henry I and a canon of St Paul's. It was intended for the care of the sick and the

M

relief of travellers and pilgrims. It is noteworthy that St Bartholomew's cared for pregnant women until delivered of their babies and, whether or not it reflects the maternal death rate of the times, orphans were maintained at this hospital until they reached the age of seven years. Soon after its foundation, the staff were given permission to choose their own warden under the supervision of the Prior of St Bartholomew's Priory. Later, at the end of the twelfth century, the hospital developed independently of the priory and was beginning to acquire property, grants of money and bequests which it was able to administer without any reference to the prior. St Bartholomew's Hospital is known to have accommodated sufferers from epilepsy, paralysis, dropsy, fevers and insanity in addition to those patients presenting eye and ear disorders.

The very early foundation of St Peter's at York, as previously noted, was re-founded under the name of St Leonard's. This hospital survived for some four hundred years; when dissolved in 1540 it had become one of the largest hospitals in the country. A remarkable feature of St Leonard's was the detailed and specialised care it provided. Apart from a very large staff, more than two hundred sick could be accommodated. Moreover, a special sister was appointed to care for delicate and sick children and two cows were kept to provide them with milk.

Many hospitals employed women to nurse patients as well as for purely domestic duties and it seems worth digressing for a moment to note that there is evidence to show that some women even practised medicine, quite apart from those offering their services as nurses and midwives.

The earliest recorded woman physician appears to have been Matilda from Wallingford, Berkshire, who was practising *c* 1232. She is recorded as 'Matilda la Leche' or the 'sage femme' and was assessed much higher than any other woman in the town, indicating that she was a successful practitioner.

Agnes 'medica', from Huntingdonshire (*c* 1270), was similarly regarded as a skilled physician by her neighbours. In London, *c* 1286, there was a lady named Katherine described as 'la surgiene' suggesting she carried on some sort of medical practice. Moreover, her father and brother were also surgeons. At the very beginning of the fourteenth century, Margery, a leech from Hales, Worcestershire, practised her profession, though in such a manner as to risk suspicion of witchcraft![30]

In London, St Mary of Bethlehem Hospital, founded in 1247, was originally intended for the sick but later developed a speciality for the care of the insane and became a lunatic asylum by the end of the fourteenth century. General hospitals frequently admitted the insane alongside the ordinary sick and Holy Trinity Hospital at Salisbury even cared for those mentally disturbed under the same roof with women in childbirth. It is difficult, however, before the end of the fourteenth century to identify any special provision being made for the mentally sick.

The hospital at Welton in Northumberland, founded in 1266, is interesting in that it catered for sick people visiting the holy and medicinal well situated there. It was destroyed by the Scots about 1296.[31]

Many hospitals began to decline towards the end of the thirteenth century due, in no small part, to the difficulties of maintaining financial support. Patrons died or ceased to ensure adequate provision in their wills. Much of the decline was also due to changes occurring in hospital management. Pluralism became common as wardens took up several appointments with consequent slackness in administration, and large-scale misappropriation of funds occurred. Dissatisfaction and grievances of the patients themselves became more frequent during the thirteenth and fourteenth centuries. They were unhappy about their conditions as hospital income decreased, hence the task of administration became even more difficult at precisely the time when wardens and officials were becoming absentees and non-residents of their hospitals.

The later reorganisation and maintenance of hospitals lies outside the scope of this book, but a gradual 'secularisation' took place with many hospitals being placed under the control of municipal authorities. Others, which still remained dependent upon monastic patronage, were almost certainly dissolved or fell upon the somewhat capricious charity of the reigning monarch.

8

Towards the Enlightenment

As Anglo-Saxon medical traditions slowly waned during the twelfth and thirteenth centuries, new influences began to filter into the country from the continent. The many superstitious practices of Anglo-Saxon medicine began to give way to a more rational approach to medical care. The older generations of practitioners, trained for the most part in herbalism, empirical remedies, magic and faith healing, were being replaced by physicians who were not only able to take advantage of a more formalised training now available to them, but, more significantly for the future, were able to apply a more clinical approach to their patients. Some superstition and magic remained, though assuming much less importance than hitherto, while the beginnings of a scientific trend began to emerge. Examination of the patient, even if in many cases conducted in a somewhat mechanical fashion, became the rule; and symptoms were studied and treatments varied to suit the condition of the patient.

These first steps towards a medical enlightenment or revival became possible due to translations of the Classical Greek medical works becoming available, first into Arabic and from this language into Latin. It is from these translated texts rather than from any specific Arabic medical advances that medicine began to grow out of its Dark Age of herbal lore and magic. This is not to say that Arabic physicians contributed nothing. Their teaching of astrology and drug therapy, for example, gained widespread currency, but nevertheless, was not anything like so important to the awakening medical world as the revival of Greek medical practices.

The Arabs, having absorbed Greek culture from their invasions and occupations of the Middle East, soon began to translate into Arabic a more pure strain of Classical material, in addition to adopting the superior medical traditions of their captive populations. Much of the medical knowledge so acquired was, in turn, rendered into Latin by such scholars as Constantinius Africanus and Gerard of Cremona in the eleventh and twelfth centuries. For example, Constantine, before 1090, had translated into Latin the Arabic version of Galen's *Art of Medicine* and *Therapeutics* as well as the medical treatises of the Moslem writer Haly Abbas, famed for his work on ophthalmology. Other works by Galen and Hippocrates were also being made available to European physicians by Jewish and Arab translators and by the thirteenth century, the revival of Greek medicine, coupled with the great influence that the medical school at Salerno exercised, ushered in a new age of medical practice.

These Arabic versions of Classical medical treatises dominated European medical circles for centuries to come. Equally important was the introduction by the Arabs of descriptions and accounts of diseases not recognised by their predecessors, such as smallpox and measles, while describing others with much greater precision as in the case of leprosy. On the other hand, however, side by side with the emergence of these superior concepts, Arabic influences were responsible for the introduction of astrology into medicine and its popularity became so great that no physician could possibly flourish without a detailed knowledge of celestial movement and the varying positions of the heavenly bodies.[1]

Traces of superstition certainly persisted from earlier times and, while much of the more absurd aspects of Anglo-Saxon medicine had disappeared, some Christian charms and a few pagan rituals remained as did the use of amulets and the belief in both the transference of disease and miraculous healing.

Astrological calculations were thought absolutely necessary to determine the appropriate time to commence or change treatment and planetary movements were regarded as strongly influencing the prognosis for the patient. Arabic medicine taught that the various parts of the body were controlled by different signs of the zodiac and the most detailed and complex astrological computations were undertaken by the physician in order to attempt a diagnosis; moreover, these computations were thought to indicate which treatment was appropriate to the particular illness. In this way a rather rigid system of medical care evolved, combining a knowledge of astrology with Galen's teaching of the bodily 'humours' and 'elements' or 'qualities'.

Medieval medicine was profoundly influenced by this combination which, simply put, involved the hypothesis that health depended upon an equilibrium being established between the four bodily qualities, earth, fire, air and water, and the corresponding four humours, melancholia, cholera, blood and phlegm. Earth was regarded as cold and dry, fire as hot and dry, air as hot and moist and water as cold and moist. Thus the melancholic patient was cold and dry, the choleric, hot and dry, the sanguine, hot and moist and the phlegmatic, cold and moist. Disease, therefore, was thought to be caused by an excess of one of the four humours which treatment was expected to reduce.

Once in possession of his list of planetary movements, eclipses of sun and moon and many other astrological data, the physician could soon determine the illness from which his patient suffered and the treatment which was indicated to reduce the disturbance of the humours.

The medical practitioner, when called in to a patient, would first calculate from which combination of humours the disease had originated and, as each disease was thought to be influenced by the course of the moon and the various signs of the zodiac, the treatment was thereby prescribed for each phase or position of the planets and stars. The physician would inquire as to when the illness began and then look up the position the moon had occupied at that time. In addition, the patient's date of birth and other personal details were taken into account before any diagnosis, prognosis or treatment was attempted. The physician believed that his calculations would inform him of the progress of the illness and if a crisis could be expected. His choice of medicines would depend largely upon the position of the stars at any particular time and would therefore vary frequently; indeed, it was believed that medicines employed without the benefit of astrological data were of little use.

Despite the domination of such formalised and mechanical ideas and theories of the humours and elements, planets and signs, books were being written by a small group of English practising physicians which, while not entirely free from astrology and superstition, showed considerable advances in clinical observation and examination while prescribing more rational and effective treatments. It is to some of these works and their authors that the remainder of this chapter is devoted.

Before examining in some detail the work of these practitioners who were, after all, the intellectual élite of their age, a brief look at the activities of the ordinary physician through contemporary eyes may be of interest.

It is fairly certain that apart from those engaged by leading families who could afford to retain a physician on their staff, many of the more humble practitioners were more likely to be itinerant and in the smaller villages many remedies must have been prepared by the housewife, no doubt acting upon old folk tradition. There were, however, without doubt, physicians in local practice in many towns and it is probable that, as time went by, those who worked an itinerant practice became more established as towns grew and populations increased.

The impression survives that the medical profession was

much concerned with making money and practising among the richer section of society. Pope Innocent II in 1139 prohibited the clergy from the study of medicine and, similarly, in 1163 at the Council of Tours monks were forbidden to absent themselves from their monasteries for longer than two months and were not permitted to teach or practise medicine. All these sanctions were clearly intended to prevent financial abuse from the medical services provided by clerical practitioners. Such rules must have been widely evaded, for in 1215 Pope Innocent III objected to the clergy spending time in the study of medicine and also prohibited them from performing any surgery involving the shedding of blood. A noteworthy departure from these prohibitions, though not unique, was that of the royal surgeon, William, of the diocese of Lincoln, who practised around 1233–54. He is the first royal surgeon known since the Conquest and it would seem that surgery was still practised even in the highest places.[2]

That physicians were fond of earning high fees is testified by several contemporary observations. They are frequently noticed as being richly dressed, indicating a relatively high social position, and it has even been suggested that such was the greed of physicians that gold was prescribed as medicine in order to charge exorbitant fees.[3] Further, John of Salisbury is recorded as having said: 'You will always hear physicians advising one another as follows: "take your fee while the patient still feels ill".'[4]

In spite of the generally held belief in the high earnings enjoyed by physicians, not all were men of social rank or comfortably off, and Chaucer's 'Doctour' may well represent the very highest stratum of his profession. Impoverished doctors certainly existed whose social status in their towns was considered even lower than the blacksmith, and considerably lower than that of the local merchants and clergy.[5] The fact that a physician, Adam of Southampton, was compelled in about 1225 to institute court proceedings to recover his fee of 20 shillings for treatment given must be indicative that his profession was liable to bad debts; moreover, it would seem that a fair amount of treatment was involved for this fee, as John Gyreberd of Hereford in 1289 only earned 6s 8d for attending to two patients, servants of the Bishop of Hereford.[6] Furthermore, John of Newbury, about 1227, had to find a surety to guarantee payment of his tax, which strongly implies a real lack of resources.[7]

While not all physicians were fully trained during the twelfth to thirteenth centuries, those who did embark upon a medical education found it entirely in the traditions and methods applicable to other studies and disciplines such as law and theology. The medical texts used were treated in much the same fashion as religious works, repeatedly read, analysed and discussed but never materially altered. The medical student learned his texts by heart, rarely questioning the concepts upon which the texts relied, let alone the very basis upon which his subject rested. He learned his material in a purely theoretical manner, seldom if ever associating it with the practical side of his craft. In this way, his only medium of instruction was through books and theoretical lectures.

In the medical schools of the twelfth to fourteenth centuries, formal lectures were delivered based upon the works of Galen, Hippocrates and other classical authors, gradually extending in scope to take in the work of such writers as Constantine, Rhases and Avicenna. The student's ability to debate his subject was often regarded as more important than any factual knowledge gained, and hence the medical man of this period was much more a theoretician than a practitioner in the modern sense of the word.

Despite the almost total lack of clinical instruction, the physician did acquire practical experience, even if only at his patient's expense! He was reputed to be expert in the use of diets, for instance, as well as being skilled in the gathering of herbs and their manufacture into medicines, always of course under the favourable influence of the stars.[8] This herbal lore still survived from earlier Saxon practices and, in fact, herbal remedies are still popular today in some quarters. It is interesting to note that some physicians evidently grew their herbs in private herb gardens, for in 1266 a Jewish physician, Solomon of Norwich, possessed his own herb garden, thought to be the earliest known in the country.[9]

By the end of the thirteenth century, medical practice was finally separating into its two branches of medicine and surgery and Chaucer's 'Doctour' was seemingly regarded as equally proficient in both,[10] while John of Gaddesden claimed considerable skill in bone setting and was certainly interested in new methods of treating compound fractures.[11]

By this date also it was becoming increasingly necessary for physicians to be men possessing some learning in their craft. For instance, Bartolomeus Anglicus (Bartholomew), in his medical treatise *De proprietatibus rerum* (Book Seven), written about 1230–50, strongly advises that physicians keep up to date with their subjects and be especially aware that changes in the progress of a disease necessitate changes in its treatment, such advice being in marked contrast to the practice of the Anglo-Saxon leeches. The physician, Bartholomew suggests, must endeavour to diagnose with accuracy and, most significantly, he advises him to 'search and seek the cause by sight, by handling and feeling as well as by the urine and by the pulse'.[12] Bartholomew also suggests that doctors should teach their patients the use of baths, bloodletting and certain medicines as well as the beneficial effects to be gained from moderate exercise.[13]

Bartholomew, at least, possessed some feeling for his patients, for he strongly advocates that the physician should, at all times, be of an optimistic nature and ever hopeful for the restoration of good health; he should also assure the patient that only what is necessary will be done and then performed as gently as possible. Should no hope remain for his patient, he should be allowed to eat and drink whatever he desires.[14]

ENGLISH MEDICAL AUTHORS *c* 1230–1310

A great deal of the medical writing undertaken in the twelfth to fourteenth centuries was really little more than the copying of earlier compilations from various English and foreign sources; even in the few substantial works, the texts are in effect no more than surveys of received medical practice of the time. There is little evidence of any research or originality and a strong reliance is always placed upon the work of predecessors, large parts of which are borrowed one from the other. An apparent wide acquaintance with illness together with a serious lack of detail in observation seems to be typical of the medieval physician.

It is now intended to discuss, in a necessarily fragmentary way, three of the principal English medical authors and their work in order to illustrate how, as was claimed at the beginning of the chapter, medicine was beginning to reflect an increasing degree of rational treatment, some slight, though definite evidence of clinical observation and the adoption of some discrimination in prescribed treatment. A start was being made to lift medical practice out of its earlier debased position and though profound advances were not yet in sight, solid gains were beginning to emerge.

The three physicians chosen whose English nationality is certain are Bartolomeus Anglicus (Bartholomew) who wrote his *De proprietatibus rerum* about 1230–50, Gilbertus Anglicus (Gilbert) and his *Compendium Medicinae* written about 1240 and John of Gaddesden whose work the *Rosa Anglica* dates from about 1314. Some reference will also be made to Bernard of Gordon's *Lilium Medicinae*, written in 1303, for while Bernard's origin is obscure, he is thought to have been of Scottish descent.

BARTOLOMEUS ANGLICUS

Bartholomew was a member of the Franciscan order and by 1225 was a professor of theology in Paris. He wrote his encyclopaedic work *De proprietatibus rerum*, 'Concerning the properties of things', in about 1230–50, and it is its seventh section which deals with medical matters. The whole work became extremely popular as is testified by the number of manuscripts still surviving in the libraries of Europe and it has even been suggested that in its time it was the most widely read work apart from the Bible.[15] The principal purpose of the seventh book concerning medicine was not so much as a textbook, though it may well have been useful in this direction, but rather for use by members of his order in their work among the population. It was intended as a kind of encyclopaedia of contemporary medical knowledge for those able to transmit it to the general public.

An important feature of Bartholomew's work is that although he frequently names his sources of information, he makes few references to the use of drugs, as if he was aware of their danger in non-professional hands.[16] Some of his authorities were, of course, the giants of the medical world upon whom so much medieval medicine depended. Constantine the African, Alexander of Tralles, Haly Abbas, Avicenna and Isidore of Seville are just some of Bartholomew's sources and hence his work provides a valuable and concise compilation of medical knowledge circulating during the twelfth and thirteenth centuries.

It should not be thought, however, that Bartholomew indiscriminately followed his sources. When discussing headache, for instance, he quotes the view of both Galen and Constantine that its cause was due, amongst other things, to phlegm at the back of the head, but insists that there were far more likely causes of this condition. He was well aware that excess of wine was a very common reason for the onset of headache!

Bartholomew evidently thought himself well versed in the management of mental illness and devotes two sections to the subject. He recognised the danger of hydrophobia from the bite of a mad dog and he regarded depression as the result of prolonged grief or overwork. He was also aware that mental illness had many causes and a variety of symptoms. 'For some cry and leap and hurt and wound themselves and others like some dark place and hide themselves in secret places,'[17] these latter signs being typical of the melancholic and depressed.

There is a remarkably modern attitude in Bartholomew's treatment of the mentally sick. He still advises binding up the insane, but only to prevent them from hurting themselves. He then goes on to recommend that such patients should be comforted and encouraged to give up 'busy thoughts' (over-work and preoccupation) and removed from their predis-posing environment – a very modern concept. He goes even further and prescribes that the patient 'be gladdened with instruments of music and some deal be occupied', which certainly has a modern ring to it.[18] Occupational therapy has become a routine treatment for the psychiatric patient only in recent years and the use of music therapy is even now only in its infancy. Significantly, in this large and detailed account about insanity and mental illness, nothing is said about evil spirits and devil possession; a big leap forward, but one which unfortunately was not to be sustained.

Finally, he recommends that if all treatment proves un-successful in cases of mental illness, surgery may have to be performed and this, surely, projects him many centuries into the future; furthermore he recognises the anaesthetising properties of mandrake in surgery and the dangers to life from its overdose.

Arthritis evidently remained a problem, for most of the medical texts deal with it at some length. Bartholomew defines arthritis as 'an ache and disease in the fingers and toes with swelling and pain',[19] and distinguishes arthritis of the hands from that of the feet which he regards as podagra or gout. The arthritic symptoms, according to Bartholomew, are redness, heat and swelling of the affected part. More remarkable is his insight into its causes. 'Arthritis comes from the age of the patient and from the region in which he lives and from the climate . . .'[20] No elderly sufferer from arthritis will deny the truth of these comments! Even more extraordinary for his time, Bartholomew provides a clear differential diagnosis between osteo- and rheumatoid arthritis. Of the latter, he says, 'One form of the disease is worse for it makes the fingers shrink and shrivels the toes and sinews of the feet and of the hands. This form . . . makes the hands dry and crooked and closed and incapable of being opened. Also it makes the joints of the fingers unsightly with knotty bunches and this sickness must be treated soon, for when it is old it is only curable with difficulty . . .'[21] A more accurate description of rheumatoid arthritis of the hands and feet is hard to imagine.

To conclude this passing review of Bartholomew's work, it is of interest to consider his opinion about epilepsy or the 'falling sickness'.[22] This condition, or what was thought to be epilepsy, was evidently common, for Bartholomew, Bernard of Gordon and John of Gaddesden, amongst others, have all left lengthy accounts of it and their suggestions for its cure.

Bartholomew's theory of the causes of epilepsy reflects the medical ideas then fashionable. The humours being out of equilibrium produced a failure by the brain to transmit nerve impulses. However, when it comes to describing the illness, it is clear that he possessed a keen appreciation of its symptoms. He records that epilepsy was also called the 'children's disease' for children frequently suffer from it and goes on to say:

He that has the disease falleth suddenly. The mouth is set awry and aside and the face also. There is tremor of the neck and of the head and of the body with grinding and gnashing of the teeth and tight clenching of the teeth and foaming at the mouth and the pouring out of many superfluities [excretions].[23]

He knew of the 'aura' frequently experienced before an epileptic attack, but felt that these attacks were in some way influenced by the moon.

Bartholomew was conscious of the difficulty of treating epilepsy, but thought that medicines and diet could help.

He warns patients to avoid crowds and overeating, while ensuring bowel regularity, all sound advice; but he then succumbs to recommending such measures as the drinking of a hare's urine in order to dissolve the humours affecting the brain. Absurd though this advice is, it is in no way inferior to that of Bernard of Gordon who, half a century later, recommended the use of mistletoe or peony worn around the neck or the whispering of a narrative charm to a patient during his epileptic attack, not to mention the curious and far from readily available curds from a leopard![24]

GILBERTUS ANGLICUS

Gilbert was born about 1180 and wrote his *Compendium Medicinae* about 1240, after having studied at Salerno. He was sufficiently well known to be mentioned as one of the authorities of Chaucer's Doctour of Phisik, in company with other distinguished physicians.

The *Compendium*, the earliest complete English medical text, provides an excellent example of the state of thirteenth-century medicine.[25] It has been favourably received by physicians as it contains much less superstitious matter than the later *Rosa Anglica* of John of Gaddesden but, nevertheless, the *Compendium* recommends on occasion the use of charms, albeit apologetically, as if Gilbert himself held no high opinion of, nor much faith in, their efficacy.[26] As might be expected, in sexual matters the use of charms is reminiscent of Anglo-Saxon times. The sexually impotent must pull up certain plants while reciting the Lord's prayer and in absolute silence extract the juices while writing various words upon cards hung around the neck.

It is noticeable that, although the *Compendium* set the pattern for John's *Rosa Anglica* and Bernard's *Lilium*, Gilbert's work is distinguished by containing numerous sections on surgery in marked contrast to Bernard's text in which surgical material is almost totally absent while the *Rosa* merely touches the subject. This is not to suggest that Gilbert was a practising surgeon, but his surgical chapters are as complete a picture as we have of contemporary surgical art, excepting possibly that surviving from Italy.

To some extent Gilbert preserves the older traditions of polypharmacy, yet he is careful to insist that a physician should not only learn from his predecessors but should discover for himself the best treatments by study and practice.

The *Compendium* is divided into seven books dealing with diseases from the head to feet after the custom of the day. They deal with such conditions as fevers, afflictions of head and brain, diseases of the eyes and ears, of the respiratory organs, stomach, intestines, liver, spleen and kidneys. The final book concerns diseases of the generative organs but also contains important chapters on leprosy, measles and small-pox. Bernard's *Lilium* covers much the same ground, also in seven books, and clearly uses Gilbert as a guide.

It was common at this time to attach great importance to the value of diets and Gilbert was no exception, while the examination of urine was also given some emphasis in his management of fevers, once again reflecting contemporary diagnostic concepts. It is interesting to note in the book on fevers that venesection, though sparingly recommended, is never to be attempted during the Egyptian Days and on certain other dates, all harking back to advice given in the Anglo-Saxon texts which, in turn, as we have seen, preserve the rules laid down in Hippocratic times. Similarly, blood-letting techniques in the treatment of arthritis are almost identical to those contained in the *Leechbook* (see chapter 5).

Like Bartholomew, Gilbert devotes a considerable section to arthritis which provides evidence of personal acquaintance with the disease and its treatment. He also recognises the different types of 'arthritis'; sciatica in the hip, pain in the hands and podagra or gout in the feet. Further, he knew that arthritis can be present in the head, spine and elsewhere 'where some humour runs down' into the part.[27]

Gilbert's account of the causes of arthritis is not as rational as that given by Bartholomew for he suggests that

N

habitual sexual excess could weaken the joints, depriving them of their natural heat and moisture, while humoural imbalance could also cause this disorder. Curiously, he maintains that neither boys nor women could be affected by gout, because boys are too young to experience sexual relations while women are passive during intercourse. He recognises that arthritis could be congenital due, he thinks, to infected semen, while flatulence as a cause of gout is suggested in the same way as Bartholomew warns against any food likely to cause wind.

Gilbert also concerns himself with hygiene and the care of one's appearance. Steam baths to soften the skin and open the pores, and washing in warm water, carefully drying the skin, are suggested. Pale cheeks may be improved with a lotion of 'Brazil-wood chips' soaked in rose water, or conversely, if the face is too red, the root of cyclamen will blanch the skin.

Freckles, moles, wrinkles, warts and other skin blemishes are all discussed as well as halitosis and bodily odours which strongly imply that the seeking after artificial beauty aids is no new phenomenon.[28]

To assist travellers, Gilbert prescribes frequent bathing, plenty of sleep and the avoidance of extremes of temperature. Breakfast should be light, while a full evening meal is allowed but only after a period of rest.

The care of the feet is considered in the detail expected in view of the mode of travel then encountered. They should be vigorously rubbed with salt and vinegar and then an ointment of nettle juice and mutton fat should be applied or, alternatively, a mixture of garlic, soap and oil may be used.

To prevent seasickness, pomegranate or lemon juice is prescribed while sweets may be sucked or aromatic seeds chewed. As food was necessarily salted, it is suggested in cases of seasickness that whatever is eaten should be well cooked in frequent changes of water before being left to soak in fresh water to ensure the removal of all traces of preservative which might irritate the stomach.

The treatment of wounds occupies the main surgical portion in the *Compendium* and fractures of the skull are dealt with in some detail. Gilbert seems quite clear about the various possible degrees of head injury and he instructs the surgeon accordingly.

Wounds of the trachea and oesophagus he regards as fatal, as are wounds of the heart, stomach and diaphragm, though those of the chest may be cared for with albumen dressings.

A most remarkable section is that which describes in minute detail what could now be called transplant surgery of the intestines. While Gilbert follows Roger of Parma in the technique of transplanting a canula or tube of alder-wood to replace a perforated section of intestine, he adds his own comments which suggest that at least he had an understanding of the principles involved, even if he did not develop the operation himself.[29]

Gilbert produced anaesthetics from a large number of ingredients; these were soaked up into a sponge which was placed over the patient's nose and mouth until he lost consciousness. To revive him, vinegar was rubbed on to his teeth and nostrils.[30] It is evident that by this time anaesthesia was being employed in surgery for, in addition to the anaesthetics devised by Gilbert, it will be remembered that Bartholomew had also recommended the use of mandrake in wine for reducing sensation before surgery (see chapter 5).

The *Compendium Medicinae* continues with the management of fractures and dislocations and the care of those suffering from conditions of the genital organs such as hydrocele, orchitis and 'hernia'.

The final word on Gilbert's work will concern his account of smallpox which is of some importance. It has been seen in chapter 3 how smallpox is thought to have been responsible for some, at least, of the 'pestilences' recorded in early English history and its ravages were such that the disease was included in most of the medieval medical texts.

A long description of the causes and varieties of smallpox

is given, though in the fashion of the times, but Gilbert's description of its symptoms are realistic. High fever, blood-shot eyes, pain in the throat and chest, cough and skin irritation are all noted. He recognises the dangers of complications such as ulceration of the eyes, throat and lungs, while ulceration of the intestines can result in a serious form of diarrhoea.

He advocates tying the patient's hands to prevent scratching, so reducing the risk of skin pitting or pock marks, and suggests drinks of whey and the use of saffron (crocus) as beneficial.

More significant, however, is the fact that Gilbert was the first writer to indicate the use of red colour in the treatment of smallpox, a procedure later to be actually adopted by John of Gaddesden when treating Edward II's son, with satisfactory results.

Gilbert's *Compendium* without doubt exerted a considerable influence upon the future of surgery, no less than of medicine, for in spite of the relatively poor level of both, he must be given the credit for laying the foundations of a great deal of medical and surgical writing that was to come after him.

JOHN OF GADDESDEN

John, born in Little Gaddesden, Hertfordshire, about 1280, was educated at Oxford University and apparently was the first physician of distinction to have had his entire medical training in England. His treatise, the *Rosa Anglica*, written about 1314, became widely used and is a compilation from many previous authors due in no small part to the great respect given to received authority already noted. Bernard of Gordon's work was extensively used by John, as were those of Gilbertus Anglicus, Avicenna, Haly Abbas and Averroes. The *Rosa* is in reality a mixture of various medical theories and teachings, together with some superstitious charms, folk remedies and religious practices. John, nevertheless, became the first Englishman to hold an appointment as court physician during the reign of Edward II[31] and is another physician sufficiently distinguished to merit a mention by Chaucer in his *Prologue*.

John showed little modesty in his work for, in his introduction, he tells his readers that 'as the rose overtops all flowers, so this book overtops all treatises on the practice of medicine . . . for here they [physicians and surgeons] will find plenty about all curable diseases, both from the special and the general point of view'.

Surgery occupies little of the text and even this has been copied from previous works. There is, however, in addition to his claim to be a skilled bonesetter, the case of John personally performing an operation to remove a 'stone' from beneath his father's tongue as well as his method of reducing a dislocated jaw, both of which testify to some practical surgical experience.[32] Further evidence of personal practice is John's cure for warts. 'I have proved myself often on my own body, [the cure] is to rub agrimony on them frequently and bruise [the plant] with salt and vinegar . . .'[33]

An interesting survival from earlier herbal lore is John's advice to the weary traveller. Ragweed or artemisia in wine or broth is recommended as a refreshing drink. The *Leechbook of Bald* similarly prescribes artemisia, though this time placed inside the traveller's shoe.[34]

Other ancient survivals in the *Rosa* concern such sympathetic magical practices as applying pigeons' droppings mixed with honey to the back of the head of a patient with lethargy or mental confusion. A robin's heart tied around the neck was supposed to prevent sleep, a state John considers to be avoided at all costs for those suffering from lethargy and, finally, a heart from a robin and an owl placed together above the patient would cure his insomnia.[35] It should be noticed that, although the *Rosa Anglica* contains many examples of magic, charms and folklore, there is hardly any evidence of astrology, but instead John boasts knowledge and skill in the art of physiognomy.[36]

John is well known for his famous treatment of Edward

II's son. He improved upon Gilbert's advice on the use of red colour by surrounding the prince with a scarlet cloth, and he tells us, 'I permitted only red things to be about his bed, by which I cured him, without leaving a trace of the small-pox pustules on him.'[37] Here again he was not original, as Bernard of Gordon had suggested wrapping the body in a red cloth some ten years previously.

John's chapter on epilepsy also contains more than a hint of Bernard's work.[38] Among the many suggestions for its treatment are examples of the persistence of sympathetic magic in the text. To reduce the period of the epileptic attack, John advises the wearing of a cuckoo's head around the neck, particularly for children unable to take medicine. This advice is sound, he claims, for as the cuckoo itself is subject to monthly attacks of epilepsy, its head will thereby attract the disease to itself.

John's prescriptions are frequently of great length, in contrast to his very practical advice for dealing with an actual epileptic fit. 'During the paroxysm, the feet should be rubbed with salt, his head should be elevated and the foam wiped from his mouth.'[40]

The *Rosa Anglica* sub-divides arthritis into three groups, much as in Bartholomew's text. 'Sciatica' or pain around the hip, 'podagra' or pain in the joints of the feet and 'cheiragra', defined as pain in the hands and fingers.

Its causes, John suggests, include the eating of 'windy' foods, constipation and overeating at night followed by intercourse. He makes great play of the sexual involvement in the cause of arthritis, and quotes Galen as saying that eunuchs never suffer from podagra; he considers adolescents similarly free from it.

John's account of paralysis displays a considerable degree of rational observation and knowledge, an awareness that paralysis may assume many different forms. 'Sometimes the entire half of the body is afflicted, from the head to the foot . . . and prevents speech, that is called general paralysis, sometimes it affects one foot only, or the finger only and that is called partial paralysis.'[41] The causes of paralysis are also clear. 'Falling, percussion [compression] of the nerves, attrition and cutting across the nerves, also anger, fear and excess of cold . . .'[42] John notes the difference between paralysis and cramp and offers the strange prognosis that if young people should suffer from fever and produce 'green urine', then paralysis or cramp will result.

Among the treatments offered for paralysis are medicines prepared from a multitude of ingredients, mild laxatives, and massage to the limbs and to the back of the head. As with many illnesses, John advises that intercourse, drunkenness and overeating should be avoided, as should long periods in the bath and catching cold.

To confirm that John remained typical of his age, his final advice to those suffering from what he regarded as paralysis is to bathe in water 'wherein an entire fox is boiled until its flesh separate from the bones; with rue and flagflower and caraway and peony and vervain'. The paralysed limb is later to be massaged and wrapped up well in the fox's skin.[43]

CONCLUSION

In this study of random samples of Bartholomew's, Gilbert's and John's work, perhaps enough has been given to demonstrate that a more rational medical practice was evolving, even if areas of superstition, magic and primitive herbalism still persisted.

Indicated also is the certainty that large parts of these texts are copies of earlier works, particularly those of the Classical Greek authors made available through the activities of Arabic physicians and translators.

The work of Hippocrates and Galen, for example, had been almost forgotten in Europe, but was revived, improved and added to by the medical expertise of these Arabic writers. A body of medical knowledge was therefore being created which not only presented medicine in more detail and emphasised clinical observation and practice, but was incomparably superior to the rather debased and corrupted Greek medicine which was all the Anglo-Saxons and their Norman successors had available.

This improvement in European medicine, in which England shared, was to survive almost until the Renaissance when the Arabic school of medicine was, in turn, superseded. During its long period of dominance, it greatly reduced the supernatural elements hitherto so common, and many religious rites and practices were abolished. On the other hand, as has been indicated earlier in this chapter, Arabic influence increased the blind reliance upon previously received authority. The written word was held in high regard; hence the almost total reliance upon the Greek masters.

We have now traced the development of English medical practice from its almost complete dependence upon folk medicine, magic and herbalism, through its incorporation of Christian elements of faith healing and the increasing religious awareness that the sick should be cared for, to finally noting the emergence of a group of men whose work justified their description of physician and who were gradually evolving professional traditions and practices.

These men, at first untrained but for trial and error, and the example of their mentors, slowly produced not only a formal medical education for which attendance at a medical school was regarded as essential, but began to share a much more refined and compassionate vision of their work.

They and their activities provided the foundation upon which was built the ever-increasing skill and learning which so enhanced their calling in the succeeding centuries. The medical enlightenment had, without doubt, begun.

Notes and References

Chapter 1: Archaeological Evidence (pages 19–42)

1   F. G. Parsons, 'History of Modern Englishmen', *Early Man* (London, 1931), pp 76–82

2   Calvin Wells, 'Report on the Human Skeletons from Red Castle, Thetford', *Norfolk Archaeology*, XXXIV (1967), pt II, pp 155–86

3   For a full discussion of older views and hypotheses on craniometric indices which should now be treated with caution, see G. M. Morant, 'A First Study of the Craniology of England and Scotland from Neolithic to Early Historic Times', *Biometrika*, 18 (1926), pp 56–98; B. G. E. Hooke and G. M. Morant, 'British Craniology in Late Prehistoric and Historic Times', ibid, pp 99–104; K. Pearson, 'On the Coefficient of Racial Likeness', ibid, pp 115ff

4   J. Cameron, *The Skeleton of British Neolithic Man*, (London, 1934), pp 118–19. This aspect may be further pursued in the more recent study by C. B. L. Lavelle *et al*, 'Analysis of the Changes in Maxillary Dental Arch Dimensions between Anglo-Saxon and Modern Times', *Journ Dental Research*, 50, no 2 (1970), pp 409–13

5   For further details of stature in ancient populations, see N. H. Huber, 'The Problem of Stature Increase', *The Skeletal Biology of Earlier Human Populations*, ed D. R. Brothwell (London, 1968)

6   Calvin Wells, report on the human remains in 'An Anglo-Saxon Cemetery at Little Eriswell, Suffolk', *Proc Camb Antiq Soc*, 59 (1966)

7   G. M. Knocker, 'Early Burials and an Anglo-Saxon Ceme-

tery at Snell's Corner, near Horndean, Hampshire', *Hants Field Club & Archaeol Soc*, 19, pt 2 (1958)

8   K. Pearson, *Archaeologia*, 73 (1923), p 109

9   J. C. Brash, 'An Anglo-Saxon Cemetery at Bidford-on-Avon, Warks', *Archaeologia*, 73 (1923).

10 A. E. Miles, 'The Dentition of the Anglo-Saxons', *Proc Roy Soc Med*, 62 (1969), pp 1311–15

11 J. Cameron, pp 179ff

12 L. H. D. Buxton, 'Platymeria and Platycnemia', *Journ of Anatomy* (1938), 73 (1), pp 31–6

13 For this and subsequent references to the North Elmham community, I am indebted to Dr Calvin Wells for information in a personal communication

14 Calvin Wells, *Norfolk Archaeology*

15 A. E. W. Miles, *Proc Roy Soc Med*, 62 (1969). See also same author's 'Assessment of the Ages of a Population of Anglo-Saxons from their Dentition', *Proc Roy Soc Med*, 55 (1962), pp 881–6

16 A. L. Meaney and S. C. Hawkes, *Two Anglo-Saxon Cemeteries at Winnall*, Medieval Archaeology, Monograph Series No 4, p 20

17 J. C. Russell, 'Population in Europe 500–1500', *Fontana Economic History of Europe*, ed C. M. Cipolla, vol 1 (1972), p 47

18 A detailed account of Harris's lines and their application to juvenile morbidity may be found in C. Wells, 'A New Approach to Palaeopathology: Harris's Lines', *Diseases in Antiquity*, ed D. R. Brothwell and A. T. Sandison (Springfield, U.S.A. 1967). See also C. Wells, 'A New Approach to Ancient Disease', *Discovery* 22, pp 526–31 and *Bones, Bodies and Diseases* (London, 1964). The cautionary note is contained in W. A. Marshall, 'Problems in Relating the Presence of Transverse Lines in the Radius to the Occurrence of Disease', *Skeletal Biology in Earlier Human Populations* (1968)

19 Calvin Wells, *Diseases in Antiquity*

20 *Leechbook of Bald*, I, lxi (1).

21 Calvin Wells, 'Osgood-Schlatter's Disease in the Ninth Century', *Brit Med Journ* (1968), pt 2, pp 623–4

22 J. C. Trevor, 'Note on the Human Remains of Romano-British Date from Norton, Yorks', R. H. Hayes and E. Whitley, *The Roman Pottery at Norton, East Yorkshire* (Leeds, 1950)

23 Calvin Wells, 'Two Medieval Cases of Malignant Disease',

Brit Med Journ (1964), pt 1, pp 1611–12; D. R. Brothwell, 'The Palaeopathology of Early British Man', *Journ Roy Anthrop Inst*, 91 (1961), pp 318–44

24 W. J. Moore and M. E. Corbett, 'The Distribution of Dental Caries in Ancient British Populations (1) Anglo-Saxon Period', *Caries Research*, 5 (1971), pp 151–68

Chapter 2: Medical Sources (pages 43–69)

1 O. Cockayne, *Leechdoms, Wortcunning and Starcraft of Early England*, 3 vols (Rolls Series, London, 1864–6), hereafter cited as *Leechdoms*. All the references and section numbers for prescriptions, recipes, etc cited in this present book are as published in these three volumes, except for the *Lacnunga* (see note 5 below)

2 *Leechdoms*, vol 1, pp 3ff

3 Ibid, vol 1, pp 327–73; this is the concluding part of MS Vitellius CIII

4 Ibid, vol 2; this entire volume is devoted to the *Leechbook of Bald*

5 A recent and more accurate translation of this text has been published in J. H. G. Grattan and C. Singer, *Anglo-Saxon Magic and Medicine* (London, 1952); all references to the *Lacnunga* are based upon their newer system of numbering the chapters

6 *Leechdoms*, vol 3, pp 83–145

7 Ibid, vol 1, pp 375–405; vol 3, pp 145–7

8 A full account of the history and a textual analysis of the *Anglo-Saxon Herbal* is contained in *Leechdoms*, vol 1, lxxv–lxxxii; a still useful discussion of this text can be found in J. F. Payne, *English Medicine in Anglo-Saxon Times* (Oxford, 1904), pp 65–8

9 *Anglo-Saxon Herbal*, hereafter referred to as *ASH*, xc (paras 6–16)

10 Ibid, clvi

11 Grattan and Singer, op cit, pp 80ff; Payne, op cit, pp 79ff

12 *ASH*, xxi

13 Ibid, lx

14 Ibid, lxxvii

15 Ibid, iv (2)

16 Ibid, xxvi (1)

17 Ibid, xxxi (3)

18 *Medicina de Quadrupedibus*, xiii (9)

19 *Med de Quad*, i (3)

20   Ibid, i (2)
21   *Leechdoms*, vol 2
22   Ibid, vol 2, xxxiii; W. Bonser, *Medical Background of Anglo-Saxon England* (London, 1963), pp 24–5
23   *Leechdoms*, vol 2, p 298; the first line of this verse in translation runs: 'Bald is the owner of this book, which he ordered Cild to write'
24   There are, however, some oblique references to herbal remedies in *Bede's Ecclesiastical History of the English People*, ed B. Colgrave and R. A. B. Mynors (Oxford, 1969), iv, 32 (this work is henceforth cited as *HE*, in abbreviation of its Latin title *Historia Ecclesiastica Gentis Anglorum*); also in *Felix's Life of St Guthlac*, ed B. Colgrave (Cambridge, 1956), chap liii; and in Bede's *Prose Life of St Cuthbert*, chap xxii, *Two Lives of St Cuthbert*, ed B. Colgrave (Cambridge, 1940)
25   W. Bonser, *Medical Background*, p 313; Grattan and Singer, op cit, p 81
26   *Leechbook of Bald*, I, xlii; III, xii (hereafter all references to the *Leechbook of Bald* will be cited as *LB*, followed by the book and chapter number)
27   *LB*, I, xxxvi
28   Ibid, I, lxiii
29   Ibid, II, lix
30   Ibid, I, xvii; xvi (1)
31   Ibid, I, iv (2)
32   Ibid, I, xl
33   C. H. Talbot, 'Notes on Anglo-Saxon Medicine', *Med Hist*, 9 (1965), pp 156–69
34   *LB*, II, xlvi
35   Ibid, II, xlix
36   Ibid, II, xlviii
37   Ibid, I, xliii
38   Ibid, I, xxxviii (1) and (2)
39   Ibid, III, xxix
40   Ibid, II, lxiv
41   *Asser's Life of King Alfred*, ed W. H. Stevenson (Oxford, 1904; rev ed 1959), pp 76–7
42   Ibid, see also pp 21 and 54 for earlier confirmation that the nature of Alfred's illness was unknown and could be neither diagnosed nor effectively treated by his physicians
43   *Lacnunga*, cxxxv
44   Ibid, lxxix–lxxx
45   Ibid, cxxxiii
46   Ibid, cxxxiv

47 Ibid, clxiv
48 Ibid, xxxi
49 Ibid, lxiii
50 Ibid, clxxi
51 Ibid, clxxxix
52 Grattan and Singer, op cit, p 43
53 Bede, *HE*, V, 3
54 *Lacnunga*, lxviii
55 Talbot, *Med Hist*, 9 (1965), pp 156–8
56 C. H. Talbot, *Medicine in Medieval England* (London, 1967), p 18
57 *Leechdoms*, vol 3, p 87
58 Ibid, vol 3, p 101
59 Ibid, vol 3, p 113
60 Ibid, vol 3, p 97
61 C. Singer, 'Review of Medical Literature of the Dark Ages with a New Text of about 1110', *Proc Roy Soc Med*, 10 (1917), pp 107–60
62 C. H. Talbot, *Medicine in Medieval England*, p 45
63 *Leechdoms*, vol 3, p 147
64 Ibid, vol 3, p 145
65 Ibid, vol 1, pp 375–83

Chapter 3: Religious Sources (pages 70–96)

1 Bede was not slow to provide evidence to encourage the observance of Christianity. His story of King Eadbald of Kent's bouts of madness supposedly brought on by his irregular marriage to his stepmother is a case in point. It is interesting to note, however, that such a union was not improper in pagan Teutonic tradition. See Bede, *HE*, II, 5
2 J. F. D. Shrewsbury, 'The Yellow Plague', *Journ Hist Med*, IV (1949), pp 5–47
3 Bede, *HE*, IV, 20
4 Ibid, III, 27
5 *Anonymous Life of Coelfrith*, ch 14, *Baedae Opera Historica*, ed C. Plummer (rev ed Oxford, 1966), p 393
6 Bede's *Prose Life of St Cuthbert*, ch 8, *Two Lives of St Cuthbert*, ed B. Colgrave (Cambridge, 1940)
7 *Anonymous Life of St Cuthbert*, IV, 6, Colgrave, *Two Lives*
8 Shrewsbury, 'The Yellow Plague'
9 W. P. MacArthur, 'The Identification of Some Pestilences Recorded in the Irish Annals', *Irish Hist Studies*, VI (1949), pp 169–88

10 For a discussion of these arguments, see W. Bonser, *The Medical Background of Anglo-Saxon England* (London, 1963), pp 81–3

11 *Ingulph's History of the Abbey of Croyland*, ed H. T. Riley (London, 1893), pp 31–3

12 Colgrave, *Two Lives*

13 *Eddius Stephanus' Life of Wilfrid*, ed B. Colgrave (Cambridge, 1927)

14 *Felix's Life of St Cuthlac*, ed B. Colgrave (Cambridge, 1956)

15 *Anon Life of St Cuthbert*, IV, 7; Bede's *Prose Life of St Cuthbert*, ch 25

16 *Anon Life*, II, 8; Bede's *Life*, ch 15

17 *Anon Life*, IV, 15; Bede's *Life*, ch 41

18 See also Bede, *HE*, III, 11 for another example of earth's supposed healing properties, this time concerning King Oswald of Northumbria

19 *Life of St Guthlac*, ch 41

20 *Anon Life*, IV, 5; Bede's *Life*, ch 32

21 *Anon Life*, IV, 18; see also note 45 below

22 *Life of St Guthlac*, ch 45

23 Bede's *Life*, ch 23

24 *Anon Life*, IV, 17; Bede's *Life*, ch 45

25 *Life of St Guthlac*, ch 42

26 *Anon Life*, IV, 3; Bede's *Life*, ch 29

27 *Anon Life*, IV, 16; Bede's *Life*, ch 44

28 *Life of Wilfrid*, ch 66

29 Bede, *HE*, V, 2

30 *LB*,I, xxxii (2)

31 *Life of St Guthlac*, ch 53

32 *Adamnan's Life of St Columba*, ed A. O. and M. O. Anderson (Edinburgh, 1961), Bk II, 7

33 *Anon Life*, I, 4; Bede's *Life*, ch 2

34 B. Colgrave, *Two Lives*, p 312 suggests synovitis

35 S. Plummer, 'St Cuthbert: Notes on the Examination of his Remains', *Northumberland and Durham Med Journ* (1899), pp 231–45

36 Bede's *Life*, ch 37

37 *Northumberland and Durham Med Journ*, p 240

38 *Life of St Columba*, Bk II, 18

39 *Life of King Edward the Confessor*, ed F. Barlow (Edinburgh, 1962), pp 61–2; William of Malmesbury, *Chronicle of the Kings of England*, pp 247–8

40 William of Malmesbury, *Chronicle*, p 248

41 *Life of King Edward*, pp 64–6; William of Malmesbury, *Chronicle*, p 249
42 *Life of King Edward*, pp 125–6
43 'William of Malmesbury's Vita Wulfstani', ed R. R. Darlington, *Camden Society*, vol XL (1928); translated version by J. H. F. Peile (Oxford, 1934)
44 Ibid, Bk II, ch 7
45 *The Life of St Anselm* by Eadmer, ed R. W. Southern (Edinburgh, 1962), pp 158–60
46 Ibid, p 163
47 Ibid, p 164
48 Ibid, pp 165–6
49 Bede's *Prose Life of St Cuthbert*, ch 23
50 *The Life of St Anselm*, pp 117–18
51 Ibid, p 138
52 Ibid, p 142
53 *The Life of Ailred of Rievaulx*, ed F. M. Powicke (Edinburgh, 1964), p 49; for further contemporary references to pills and tablets, see *Life of Christina of Markyate*, ed C. H. Talbot (Oxford, 1959), p 123
54 *Life of Ailred*, pp 39–41
55 Ibid, pp 29–30
56 Ibid, p 32
57 Ibid, pp 42–3
58 Ibid, p 43
59 Ibid, pp 43–4
60 Ibid, pp 54–62
61 *Life of St Hugh of Lincoln*, ed D. L. Douie and H. Farmer (Edinburgh, 1962), vol 2, pp 7–10
62 Ibid, pp 124–6
63 Ibid, p 230
64 *Life of St Anselm*, p 152
65 A very full account of most, if not all the recorded miracles attributed to St Thomas can be found in E. A. Abbott, *St Thomas of Canterbury, His Death and Miracles*, 2 vols (London, 1898)

Chapter 4: The Physician and His Treatment (pages 97–128)

1 MS Brit Mus Harley 5294 (12th cent); MS Durham Cathedral Library, Hunter 100 (c 1100)
2 *LB*, I, xlv (5); lxxii; xlvii (3)
3 *LB*, II, lxv (2)
4 Bede, *HE*, IV, 19

5   Ibid, V, 3
6   William of Malmesbury, *Chronicle of the Kings of England*, ed
    J. A. Giles (London, 1847), p 353
7   *Saga of Magnus the Good* from *Heimskringla, Saga of the Norse
    Kings* by Snorri Sturlusson, trans S. Laing (London, rev ed
    1961), pp 148–9
8   Ibid
9   Bede, *HE*, IV, 19
10 William of Malmesbury, *Vita Wulfstani*, ed R. R. Darlington,
    p 28
11 *Asser's Life of King Alfred*, pp 21, 54
12 *Vita Wulfstani*, pp 35–6
13 The smile on the face of a doctor's assistant as he carries a
    purse containing his master's fees plainly indicates their
    fondness of money. MS Ashmole 399, fol 34v, Bodleian
    Library, Oxford
14 Bede, 'Penitential', J. T. McNeill and H. M. Gaimer,
    Medieval Handbooks of Penance (New York, 1938), p 225
15 For example, MS Bodleian Library, Oxford, Ashmole 399
16 *LB*, II, lix (11)
17 William of Malmesbury, *Chronicle of the Kings of England*, p
    444
18 Bede, *HE*, IV, 32
19 *LB*, III, lxv; *Leechdoms*, vol 3, p 183
20 *LB*, I, xliii; ibid, II, lii; *ASH*, xxxvi (6), cxxxii (5)
21 *LB*, II, lxvii; see also MS 17 St John's College, Oxford, for
    section on weights and measures
22 *LB*, II, lii (3)
23 Ibid, I, lxiii; xlviii (1); ibid, III, lxii
24 King Eorcenberht of Kent, for example, in 640 ordered the
    destruction of idols (Bede, *HE*, III, 8), and towards the end
    of the 7th century, King Wihtred found it necessary to forbid
    the making of offerings to devils (Wihtred 12–13). Alfred,
    Edward the Elder, Athelstan, Ethelred and Cnut all passed
    laws to stem the spread of paganism, in part, no doubt, due
    to Viking penetration, while law 11 of Edward and Guth-
    rum is evidence of continuing belief in wizards and sorcerers.
    Ethelred's laws frequently show concern for the persistence
    of heathen practices, eg V. Ethelred, I.34; VI. Ethelred,
    I.6; VIII. Ethelred, 44; IX. Ethelred, I; and II. Cnut, 5.1
    forbids the worship of idols, heathen gods, the sun, moon,
    fire or water. Later still, in 1075, Archbishop Lanfranc
    legislated that the bones of dead animals must not be hung
    up in order to drive away pestilence from cattle. In addition,

soothsaying and sorcery were prohibited. As late as 1126, a
papal legate in London had to condemn sorcery, sooth-
sayings and auguries

25 Bede's *Prose Life of St Cuthbert*, ch ix; see also Bede, *HE*, IV, 27
27 J. F. Payne, *Medicine in Anglo-Saxon Times*, pp 114–15
27 *LB*, I, lxxxvi; *ASH*, xi (1)
28 *Lacnunga*, lxxxiii
29 Ibid, clxviii
30 Ibid, xciii
31 *LB*, I, lxiv
32 Ibid, I, xlv (5)
33 Ibid, I, xlv (3–4)
34 Ibid, I, lxv; further examples of liturgical charms: ibid, I,
    xlvii (1); ibid, II, lxv (1) and (5); *Lacnunga*, xxvii, xxix and
    xxxi
35 *LB*, I, lxii (3)
36 Ibid, I, lxiii
37 Bede, *HE*, III, 11
38 *Leechdoms*, vol 1, p 393
39 *Lacnunga*, xciii
40 Ibid, clxvi
41 *Med de Quad*, v (12)
42 *ASH*, xix (5)
43 *Med de Quad*, iv (17); *LB*, III, ii (1)
44 *Med de Quad*, ix (12)
45 Ibid, i (3)
46 *LB*, I, xxxix (3)
47 Ibid, III, i
48 *ASH*, x (2)
49 *LB*, III, lviii
50 Ibid, I, xxxii (2)
51 Ibid, III, xxiv (1); *Leechdoms*, vol 3, p 293
52 *Lacnunga*, clxxi; lxxxi
53 Ibid, cxxxiii
54 *LB*, I, xxxix (3)
55 *Lacnunga*, cxxiii; clxii; *ASH*, clx; *LB*, II, lxv
56 *LB*, III, lvii
57 Ibid, II, lxv (5); *ASH*, clxxxii (2)
58 *Lacnunga*, xiv; lxxviii; cxxxv; *ASH*, cxxxii (1)
59 *LB*, I, xxxix (3); xxxii (2)
60 *Lacnunga*, xxvi
61 Ibid, xciii
62 *Med de Quad*, i (5); xiii (10)
63 *LB*, III, lxiii

64   *Lacnunga*, v; *LB*, I, ii (12)
65   *Life of St Guthlac* by Felix of Crowland, trans B. Colgrave
     (Cambridge, 1956), ch liii, p 167; Adamnan's *Life of St
     Columba*, ed A. O. and M. O. Anderson (Edinburgh, 1961),
     p 341
66   *LB*, I, ii (21)
67   *Lacnunga*, viii; ix; xiii
68   *Peri-Didaxeon*, 25, 26
69   *ASH*, lxiii (2)
70   *Med de Quad*, iv (4); ix (7); *LB*, III, xxxvii
71   *Lacnunga*, clxix
72   *ASH*, cxvi (2); lxxx (3); xix (4)
73   Ibid, cl
74   *LB*, III, xxxviii (1)
75   *Med de Quad*, ii (17)
76   *LB*, I, lxx
77   Roger of Hoveden's *Chronicle*, trans H. T. Riley (London,
     1853), vol 1, p 204
78   Caesarius of Heisterbach, *Dialogue of Miracles*, trans H. von
     E. Scott and C. C. Swinton Bland, 2 vols (London, 1929),
     vol 1, p 309
79   *Lacnunga*, lxxvi; *LB*, I, xvii; xxvi; xli
80   *LB*, I, xxxii (2)
81   *LB*, III, xlviii
82   *The Life of Ailred of Rievaulx*, ed and trans F. M. Powicke
     (Edinburgh, 1950), pp 49, 34
83   *LB*, III, xx
84   *Life of Ailred*, p 49
85   *Life of Christina of Markyate*, ed and trans C. H. Talbot
     (Oxford, 1959), pp 123, 125
86   *LB*, II, lvi (3)
87   Ibid, III, xxi; see also the use of the castor oil 'purgative
     seeds' in *Lacnunga*, xlii; xlvii
88   *LB*, II, lvi (2)
89   *Lacnunga*, xxxix
90   *LB*, I, xxx; *Peri-Didaxeon*, 45
91   *LB*, I, lxvi
92   Ibid, III, xli
93   Ibid, III, xl
94   Bede, *HE*, III, 11; see also *Life of St Guthlac*, ch xli
95   *Life of Ailred of Rievaulx*, p 80
96   *LB* II, xxiii
97   *Leechdoms*, vol 3, p 145
98   *Peri-Didaxeon*, 52, 53

Chapter 5: *Surgery* (*pages 129–49*)

1 Bede, *HE*, IV, 19
2 Ibid, V, 6
3 *Eddius' Life of Wilfred*, ed B. Colgrave (Cambridge, 1927), ch 23
4 *LB*, I, xxvi
5 Ibid, I, xxv (2)
6 Ibid, I, i (15)
7 *ASH*, i (2)
8 *LB*, II, xxxiii (2)
9 Ibid, I, xxxviii; ibid, III, xxxii
10 Ibid, I, xxxviii (3)
11 Ibid, I, xxxviii (8)
12 Ibid, I, lx; ibid, III, xxix; *ASH*, iii (8); lxxv (7); *Med de Quad*, xi (12)
13 *LB*, I, lx (1)
14 Ibid, I, lx (2)
15 Ibid, III, xxix
16 Ibid, II, xxii
17 C. H. Talbot, 'Notes on Anglo-Saxon Medicine', *Med Hist*, 9 (1965), pp 165–6
18 *LB*, I, xxxv
19 *ASH*, cxxxii (2)
20 Ibid, liv (3)
21 *LB*, I, lxxxii
22 *ASH*, clviii
23 *Life of St Kentigern*, p 35, *The Historians of Scotland*, vol V, ed A. P. Forbes (Edinburgh, 1874)
24 *LB*, I, xiii
25 Ibid, III, lxxiii
26 In addition to references of suturing with silk in the Icelandic Sagas, there is an unusual Northern example of the means by which large wounds could be closed. *The Danish History of Saxo Grammaticus*, ed O. Elton and F. Y. Powell (London, 1894), pp 243–4, written *c* 1200, describes a fight in which Starkad was injured so that 'most of his bowels gushed out of his belly . . .'. A youth came to him and 'replaced the parts of his belly that had been torn away, and bound up with a *plait of withies* [flexible young willow branches] the mass of intestines that had fallen out'. This would obviously act rather like a modern adhesive strapping.
27 MS Bodleian Library, Oxford, Ashmole 1462 fol 10; this illustration is one of several preceding the manuscript of the *Anglo-Saxon Herbal*

28 MS Brit Mus Harley 1585 fol 9
29 *LB*, II, xxviii
30 Ibid, II, xlvi
31 Ibid, II, xxxii, xlvii, lix (4)
32 Ibid, II, xlix
33 Ibid, I, lvi (2), xxxv
34 Ibid, I, xxxv
35 *Peri-Didaxeon*, 63
36 *LB*, I, xxxviii (8)
37 MS Brit Mus Sloan 2839; MS Durham Cathedral Library, Hunter 100 fol 122R; MS Brit Mus Harley 1585 fol 9
38 MS Brit Mus Harley 1585 fol 9
39 J. W. Clark, *Observances in Use at the Augustinian Priory at Barnwell, Cambridgeshire* (Cambridge, 1897), p 201
40 *Gesta Abbatum Monasterii S. Albani*, vol 1, ed H. T. Riley, (Rolls Series 1867), pp 207–8
41 *LB*, I, xlvii (1)
42 Ibid, II, xliii
43 Ibid, I, lxxii
44 J. W. Clark, *Observances at Barnwell*, p 201
45 For references to similar abuse of the relaxation of life during the blood-letting days, see *The Chronicle of Jocelin of Brakelond*, ed H. E. Butler (Edinburgh, 1949), p 14. The view of Herbert of Losinga (1050–1119), Bishop of Norwich, is given in a letter criticising the behaviour of a monk;'. . . you are, they say, seldom seen in the cloister, often in the parlours, slow in resorting to the church, swift in resorting to the grange, you are constantly getting leave to have your blood let, constantly getting leave to have a bath'; see *The Life, Letters and Sermons of Bishop Herbert of Losinga*, ed E. M. Goulburn and H. Symonds (London, 1878)
46 M. R. James, *Walter Map's De Nugis Curialium* (London, 1923), Hon Soc of Cymmrodorion, pp 252–3
47 Caesarius of Heisterbach, *The Dialogue of Miracles*, trans H. von E. Scott and C. C. Swinton Bland (London, 1929), vol 2, p 175
48 Bede, *HE*, V, 3
49 A full discussion of Anglo-Saxon medical vocabulary may be found in C. Lambert, 'The Old English Medical Vocabulary', *Proc Roy Soc Med* (1940), xxxiii, pp 137–45; also W. Bonser, 'Anglo-Saxon Medical Nomenclature', *English and Germanic Studies*, vol 4 (1951–2), pp 13–19
50 For a detailed analysis of the laws and currencies concerned with the compensations for injury, see S. Rubin, 'Compensa-

tion for Injury in Anglo-Saxon Law', *Roy Coll Gen Practit Yorks Faculty Journ*, Nov 1969, pp 35–51

51 F. Pollock and F. W. Maitland, *History of English Law* (Cambridge, 1895), vol 1, p 31

52 F. L. Attenborough, *The Laws of the Earliest English Kings* (Cambridge, 1922), II Canute 49

53 The references to the clauses given in both Ethelbert's and Alfred's tariffs are cited as in F. L. Attenborough, *Laws*

54 William of Malmesbury, *Chronicle of the Kings of England*, p 279

Chapter 6: The Problem of Leprosy (pages 150–171)

1 C. Creighton, *History of Epidemics in Britain* (Cambridge, 1894), vol i, p 69

2 D. Brothwell, 'The Palaeopathology of Early British Man', *Journ Roy Anthrop Inst* (1961), 91, p 323; 'Two Early Cases of Leprosy in Gt Britain', V. Moller-Christensen and D. R. Hughes, *Man*, 52 (1962), pp 177–9

3 *Chronicon Abbatiae de Evesham*, ed W. Dunn Macray (London, RS 1863), p 85; *Chronicon Abbatiae Rameseiensis*, ed W. Dunn Macray (London, RS 1886), pp 157–8

4 Bartolomeus Anglicus, *De propietatibus rerum*, under chapter on 'Leprosy'. Translation of Book 7 'On Medicine' by J. J. Walsh, *Medical Life*, 40 (1933)

5 Ibid

6 John of Gaddesden, *Rosa Anglica* under 'Leprosy'

7 Mathew Paris, *Chronica Majora* (London, RS 1874), ed H. R. Luard, vol 2, p 130; J. A. Giles (trans), *Roger of Wendover's Flowers of History* (London, 1849), vol 1, p 459

8 *Life of St Hugh of Lincoln*, ed D. L. Douie and H. Farmer (Edinburgh, 1962), vol 2, pp 11f

9 Gilbertus Anglicus, *Compendium Medicinae*, under chapter on 'Leprosy'

10 H. P. Cholmeley, *John of Gaddesden and the Rosa Medicinae* (Oxford, 1912), pp 47–8

11 R. M. Clay, *Mediaeval Hospitals of England* (2nd ed, London, 1966), p 59

12 Ibid, p 60

13 Ibid, p 184

14 Ibid, p 56

15 Calvin Wells, 'A Leper Cemetery at South Acre, Norfolk', *Medieval Archaeology*, xi (1967), pp 242–8

16 R. M. Clay, *Mediaeval Hospitals*, p 180

17 Bartolomeus Anglicus, 'Leprosy'

18 E. A. Abbott, *St Thomas of Canterbury, His Death and Miracles* (London, 1898), Vol 1, pp 306, 321 and 323

19 C. A. Mercier, *Leper Houses and Mediaeval Hospitals* (London, 1915)

20 Ibid

21 Ibid

22 Ibid

23 C. Creighton, p 90

24 Ibid, p 98

25 W. MacArthur, 'Mediaeval Leprosy in the British Isles', *Leprosy Review*, 24 (1953), p 13

26 Ibid, p 13

27 R. M. Clay, *Mediaeval Hospitals*, p 139

Chapter 7: The Monastic Infirmary (pages 172–188)

1   Bede, *HE*, IV, 24; see also ibid, III, 27

2   J. McCann, *The Rule of St Benedict* (London, 1952), ch 36

3   R. Gilyard-Beer, *Abbeys* (HMSO, 1959), p 34; R. Gilyard-Beer, *Fountains Abbey* (HMSO, 1970), p 61

4   R. L. Palmer, *English Monasteries in the Middle Ages* (London, 1930), pp 154ff

5   J. W. Clark, *Observances in Use at the Augustinian Priory at Barnwell, Cambs* (Cambridge, 1897), p 209

6   Ibid, p 207

7   Ibid, p 209

8   D. Knowles, *The Monastic Constitutions of Lanfranc* (Edinburgh, 1951), pp 119ff

9   Ibid

10 Ibid, p 89

11 Ibid

12 *Observances at Barnwell*, pp 203–5

13 *Chronica Monasterii S Albani*, ed H. T. Riley, pt IV of which is Thomas Walsingham's *Gesta Abbatum Monasterii St Albani*, vol I (London, RS 1867), pp 79–80

14 *Chronicon Monasterii de Abingdon*, ed J. Stevenson, vol II (London, RS 1855), pp 407–10

15 Bede, *Life of St Cuthbert*, ch 45, *Two Lives of St Cuthbert*, ed B. Colgrave (Cambridge, 1940)

16 'The Obedientiaries of Abingdon Abbey', *Camden Series*, vol LI (1892), p 14; further evidence of medical expenses may be found in this document: eg physicians' fees and the cost of herb collection

17 William of Malmesbury, *De Gestis Pontificum Anglorum*, ed W. E. S. A. Hamilton (London, RS 1870), p 156

18 *Chronicon Monasterii de Abingdon,* vol II, p 44

19 Ibid, p 50

20 Ibid, p 44

21 Ibid, p 287; however, other more relevant reasons for hostility to Faritius's candidature include his unpopular reputation as a clerical reformer and his Italian origin

22 *De Gestis Pontificum,* pp 437–8

23 Mathew Paris, *Chronica Majora,* ed H. R. Luard (London, RS 1872), vol II, p 668

24 Roger of Hoveden, *Chronicle,* ed H. T. Riley (London, 1853), vol I, p 227

25 *Gesta Abbatum St Albani,* vol I, pp 201–2

26 Ibid, p 246

27 *The Chronicle of Jocelin of Brakelond,* ed H. E. Butler (Edinburgh, 1949), p 96

28 D. Knowles and R. N. Hadcock, *Medieval Religious Houses* (London, 1953), p 365

29 *Eadmer's History of Recent Events in England* (Historia Novorum in Anglia), trans G. Bosanquet (London, 1964), pp 16–17

30 Eileen Power, 'Some Women Practitioners of Medicine in the Middle Ages', *Proc Roy Soc Med,* 15 (1922), pp 20–3; C. H. Talbot and E. A. Hammond, *The Medical Practitioners in Medieval England* (London, 1965), pp 211, 10, 200, 209

31 *De Gestis Pontificum,* p 156

Chapter 8: Towards the Enlightenment (pages 189–208)

1 Geoffrey Chaucer, *The Canterbury Tales,* 'The Prologue', 'Doctour of Phisik', line 414

2 C. H. Talbot and E. A. Hammond, *The Medical Practitioners in Medieval England* (London, 1965), p 375; note also Thomas de Weseham, a royal surgeon in 1252–72

3 *Canterbury Tales,* 'Prologue', lines 440, 443–4

4 John of Salisbury, *Policraticus,* ed C. C. J. Webb (Oxford, 1909), vol I, p 166; see also John of Gaddesden's strong belief that he was entitled to a good fee, and that his secret cures may be divulged for a sufficient consideration, *Rosa Anglica,* Irish Texts Society, vol xxv (1929), ed W. Wulff, p 291; all further references to Gaddesden's *Rosa* are based upon this edition of the text

5 *Medical Practitioners in Medieval England,* pp 106, 210

6 Ibid, pp 2–3, 153

7 Ibid, p 104

8 *Canterbury Tales,* 'Prologue', lines 435–7

9 M. D. Davis, *Shetaroth: Hebrew Deeds of English Jews before*

1290 (London, 1888), pp 132, 186
10   *Canterbury Tales*, 'Prologue', lines 412–13
11   H. P. Cholmeley, *John of Gaddesden and the Rosa Medicinae* (Oxford, 1912), p 58
12   Bartolomeus Anglicus, 'De proprietatibus rerum', ch LXX (pp 594–5), trans J. J. Walsh, *Medical Life* (1933), pp 453–602
13   Ibid, p 596
14   Ibid, p 597
15   J. J. Walsh, 'Medicine in a Popular Medieval Encyclopaedia', *Annals of Medical History*, 4 (1932), pp 273–82
16   'De proprietatibus rerum', pp 460–1
17   Ibid, ch VI, p 480
18   Ibid
19   Ibid, ch LVII, pp 565–6
20   Ibid
21   Ibid, p 566
22   Ibid, ch X, pp 485–8
23   Ibid, p 486
24   Bernard of Gordon, *Lilium Medicinae*, Bk II, ch XXV, 'Epilepsy'; a translation by W. G. Lennox may be found in *Annals of Medical History* (1941), pp 372–83
25   H. E. Handerson, *Gilbertus Anglicus* (Cleveland, Ohio, 1918), p 17
26   Ibid, p 27
27   Ibid, p 44
28   Ibid, pp 31–2
29   Ibid, pp 63–4
30   Ibid, p 65
31   W. Wulff, *Rosa Anglica*, p xix
32   *John of Gaddesden and the Rosa Medicinae*, p 56; C. H. Talbot, *Medicine in Medieval England* (London, 1967), p 113
33   *Rosa Anglica*, p 207
34   *LB*, I, lxxxvi
35   *Rosa Anglica*, p 235
36   I. B. Jones, 'Popular Medical Knowledge in 14th century English Literature', *Bull Hist Med*, vol V (6), 1937, p 558
37   *Rosa Anglica*, p 315
38   John of Gaddesden, 'Epilepsy', trans W. G. Lennox, *Annals of Medical History* (1939), pp 283–307
39   Ibid, p 297
40   Ibid
41   *Rosa Anglica*, p 247
42   Ibid, p 249
43   Ibid, p 267

Select Bibliography

Abbott, E. A. *St Thomas of Canterbury, His Death and Miracles*, 2 vols (London, 1898)

Anderson, A. O. and M. O. (eds). *Adamnam's Life of St Columba* (Edinburgh, 1961)

Attenborough, F. L. *The Laws of the Earliest English Kings* (Cambridge, 1922)

Barlow, F. (ed and trans). *Life of King Edward the Confessor* (Edinburgh, 1962)

Black, W. G. *Folk Medicine* (Folk-lore Society, London, 1883, Publication No 12)

Bonser, W. *The Medical Background of Anglo-Saxon England* (London, 1963)

Brothwell, D. R. (ed). *The Skeletal Biology of Earlier Human Populations* (London, 1968)

Brothwell, D. R. and Sandison, A. T. (eds). *Diseases in Antiquity* (Springfield, U.S.A., 1967)

Butler, H. E. (ed and trans). *The Chronicle of Jocelin of Brakelond* (Edinburgh, 1949)

Cameron, J. *The Skeleton of British Neolithic Man* (London, 1934)

Cholmeley, H. P. *John of Gaddesden and the Rosa Medicinae* (Oxford, 1912)

Clark, J. W. *Observances in Use at the Augustinian Priory at Barnwell, Cambridgeshire* (Cambridge, 1897)

Clay, R. M. *Mediaeval Hospitals of England* (London, 2nd ed, 1966)

Cockayne, O. (ed). *Leechdoms, Wortcunning and Starcraft of Early England*, 3 vols (Rolls Series, London, 1864-6)

Colgrave, B. (ed and trans). *Eddius Stephanus' Life of Wilfrid* (Cambridge, 1927)

——. *Felix's Life of St Guthlac* (Cambridge, 1956)

——. *Two Lives of St Cuthbert* (Cambridge, 1940)

Colgrave, B. and Mynors, R. A. B. (eds and trans). *Bede's Ecclesiastical History of the English People* (Oxford, 1969)

Creighton, C. *History of Epidemics in Britain*, vol I (Cambridge, 1894)

Darlington, R. R. (ed). 'William of Malmesbury's Vita Wulfstani', *Camden Society*, vol XL (1928)

Duoie, D. L. and Farmer, H. (eds and trans). *The Life of St Hugh of Lincoln*, 2 vols. (Edinburgh, 1962)

Giles, J. A. (trans). William of Malmesbury, *Chronicle of the Kings of England* (London, 1847)

Gilyard-Beer, R. *Abbeys* (HMSO, 1959)

Grattan, J. H. G. and Singer, C. *Anglo-Saxon Magic and Medicine* (Oxford, 1952)

Hamilton, W. E. S. A. (ed). William of Malmesbury, *De Gestis Pontificum Anglorum* (Rolls Series, London, 1870)

Handerson, H. E. *Gilbertus Anglicus* (Cleveland, Ohio, 1918)

Kirby, D. P. *The Making of Early England* (London, 1967)

Knowles, D. (ed and trans). *The Monastic Constitutions of Lanfranc* (Edinburgh, 1951)

Knowles, D. and Hadcock, R. N. *Medieval Religious Houses* (London, 1953)

McCann, J. (ed). *The Rule of St Benedict* (London, 1952)

MacKinney, L. *Medical Illustrations in Medieval Manuscripts* (London, 1965)

Palmer, R. L. *English Monasteries in the Middle Ages* (London, 1930)

Payne, J. F. *English Medicine in Anglo-Saxon Times* (Oxford, 1904)

Plummer, C. *Baedae Opera Historica* (Oxford, 1896, rev ed 1966)

Powicke, F. M. (ed and trans). *The Life of Ailred of Rievaulx* (Edinburgh, 1964)

Riley, H. T. (trans). *Ingulph's History of the Abbey of Croyland* (London, 1893)

Riley, H. T. (trans). Roger of Hoveden's *Chronicle*, 2 vols (London, 1853)

Riley, H. T. (ed). *Chronica Monasterii S Albani* (Rolls Series, London, 1867)

Russell, J. C. 'Population in Europe 500–1500', *Fontana Economic History of Europe*, vol 1, ed C. M. Cipolla (London, 1972)

Southern, R. W. (ed and trans). *The Life of St Anselm* (Edinburgh, 1962)

Stevenson, J. (ed). *Chronicon Monasterii de Abingdon*, vol 11 (Rolls Series, London, 1855)

Stevenson, W. H. (ed). *Asser's Life of King Alfred* (Oxford, 1904, rev ed 1959)

Talbot, C. H. and Hammond, E. A. *The Medical Practitioners in Medieval England* (London, 1965)

Thompson, A. Hamilton. *Bede, His Life, Times and Writings* (Oxford, 1935)

Wells, C. *Bones, Bodies and Diseases* (London, 1964)

Wulff, W. (ed). 'Rosa Anglica', *Irish Texts Society*, vol XXV (1929)

Index

P

Other 2199 55

WITHDRAWN